SENSORY PROCESSES

MATHEW ALPERN

MERLE LAWRENCE

DAVID WOLSK

The University of Michigan

BROOKS/COLE PUBLISHING COMPANY
Belmont, California

A Division of Wadsworth Publishing Company, Inc.

5 6 7 8 9 10—74 73 72 71 70

© 1967 by Wadsworth Publishing Company, Inc., Brooks/Cole Publishing Company, Belmont, California. All rights reserved. No part of this book may be reproduced in any form, by mimeograph or by any other means, without permission in writing from the publisher.

L. C. cat. card No.: 67-12818

Printed in the United States of America.

SERIES FOREWORD

Basic Concepts in Psychology was conceived as a series of brief paperback volumes constituting a beginning textbook in psychology. Several unique advantages arise from publishing individual chapters as separate volumes rather than under a single cover. Each book or chapter can be written by an author identified with the subject matter of the area. New chapters can be added, individual chapters can be revised independently, and, possibly, competitive chapters can be provided for controversial areas. Finally, to a degree, an instructor of the beginning course in psychology can choose a particular set of chapters to meet the needs of his students.

Probably the most important impetus for the series came from the fact that a suitable textbook did not exist for the beginning courses in psychology at the University of Michigan—Psychology 100 (Psychology as a Natural Science) and Psychology 101 (Psychology as a Social Science). In addition, no laboratory manual treated both the natural science and social science problems encountered in the first laboratory course, Psychology 110.

For practical rather than ideological reasons most of the original complement of authors came from the staff of the University of Michigan. As the series has developed, authors have been selected from other institutions in an effort to assure national representation and a broad perspective in contemporary psychology.

Each author in the Basic Concepts in Psychology Series has considerable freedom. He has been charged to devote approximately half of his resources to elementary concepts and half to topics of special interest and emphasis. In this way, each volume will reflect the personality and viewpoint of the author while presenting the subject matter usually found in a chapter of an elementary textbook.

CONTENTS

INTRODUCTION

Sensory psychology, the experimental analysis of how we perceive changes in our environment, is the oldest of all branches of experimental psychology. Indeed, it antedates psychology as an independent discipline by several hundred years. Perhaps this is why the questions which sensory psychologists can now pose in the laboratory are often much crisper and the answers more insightful than is yet possible in other branches of psychology. This is one of the reasons we find the field so attractive.

Because of this rich background of careful experimental study of the sense organs of man, we can take advantage of the latest tools of electrophysiology, biochemistry, and biophysics to ask penetrating questions about the sense organs of a variety of experimental animals—questions that are often at the level of the single cell. The happy result is that many of the complex processes of human sensations find an extremely close parallel, if not complete explanation, in the physical and chemical changes which we now study at the cellular level in the sense organs and/or brains of experimental animals. At no other time, and in no other branch of the sciences which study man, has it been possible to draw such striking quantitative parallels between the behavior of the normal intact organism, on the one hand, and physical and chemical events at the cellular level, on the other. This is a relatively recent development, and we have tried in these pages to capture some of its excitement. We hope it rubs off on you.

One consequence of our desire to make this book up to date is that we have decided to confine ourselves to fields in which we are actively interested and to present each chapter as an individually written discussion. Thus, you may find that the style, the assumptions, and perhaps even the approach to major questions change from one chapter to the next. There is, however, a set of underlying principles in sensory psychology which transcends such differences, and as you read these pages, it is these with which we hope to impress you.

SENSATION AND BEHAVIOR: STRUCTURE AND FUNCTION

David Wolsk

The tunicate sea squirt in its larval form swims freely about, guided by its eyes and ears, finding food and avoiding predators. Reaching adulthood, it loses its tail and attaches itself to a rock. For about two years, it sits on the rock, vegetating. Its eyes, its ears, and then its brain—all degenerate and become useless.

One of the more intriguing problems in psychology concerns the means by which an organism comes to know and to be constantly aware of its environment. Those who work in the field of sensory psychology ask a wide variety of questions about the relationship of particular aspects of the environment to particular responses of an organism—questions ranging from fine details of anatomy and biophysics to complex behavioral sequences. Sensory psychologists do not, as some men have done in the past, ponder the nature of reality. Rather than asking, "Is there a real world—apart from, or different from, that which we see, hear, and feel?" they ask, "To what range of stimuli is an organism sensitive?"

Experiments based on this question require a quantitative system for defining the stimulus—for describing in a precise and reproducible way how the physics of energy (of electromagnetic and vibratory waves) meets the responses of an organism. Generally, such a system is based in some way on the judgments of human observers.

As we shall see, a good means of quantifying stimuli enables experimenters to examine the way sensory systems function—and to find out why each responds to a certain range of a single type of stimulus energy. For instance, experiments probe deeper and deeper into the question of how light is transformed into electrical impulses in the optic nerve and why our conscious sensation is of "red" with electromagnetic radiation of one wavelength but shifts to "orange" with a slightly shorter wavelength.

SELECTIVITY

As sensory psychologists divide the environment in terms of specific stimulus energies, they find that these are related to particular behavioral sequences. For example, experiments have shown that the odor of a female moth on a piece of paper will initiate courting behavior by a male moth, though the male will ignore the sight of a nearby female if she is inside a tightly sealed glass jar.

The selective response of the male moth shows that a particular behavior sequence is determined by a specific set of stimuli or a limited aspect of a stimulus in a highly complex total stimulus situation. This selective process is characteristic of human behavior as well. It has been found that an army enlisted man, wearing lenses that distort the environment slightly, is more likely to be aware of the distortion when looking at a fellow soldier than when looking at his commanding officer.

Our appreciation of art is another example of this selective process. We form some idea of how Picasso feels about people and events from the way he selectively simplifies, distorts, and orders the environment within the confines of a frame. However, whereas every male moth will probably court the odorous piece of paper rather than the odorless female, the reactions of different people to a Picasso painting may vary from a feeling of perfect communication to complete bewilderment.

Differences between organisms—differences of selectivity, shown in stimulus-response relationships; and differences in the complexity and modifiability of sensory processing—work to the advantage of sensory psychologists as they gather extensive data from a wide variety of animal species. The anatomical, physiological, and behavioral differences between animals permit the experimenter to pick the species that most easily lends itself to the particular problem he wishes to investigate. For example, the inner ear of the guinea pig, a relatively inexpensive and easily maintained animal, is quite accessible for recording the output of the sensory cells; for behavioral studies of visual processes, pigeons are easily trained and often used. It is thus important to keep in mind the degree of "species specificity" of much sensory data.

AREAS OF STUDY

The information that sensory psychologists have amassed can be conveniently divided into nine areas: (1) the physics of sound, light, heat, and motion; (2) the chemistry of odorous and gustatory substances; (3) the gross and microscopic anatomy of receptors and neural pathways; (4) the phylogenetic and embryological development of sensory systems; (5) the electrophysiology of receptor cells; (6) the differences in patterns of neural input to the brain caused by differences in stimuli, e.g., frequency and intensity of tones; (7) the processing of neural input within the brain; (8) the quantitative measurement of the conscious sensations arising from different stimuli; and (9) the relationships between these conscious sensations and behavior. Each chapter in this book will deal with a specific sensory system and will stress different parts of this list.

The study of sensory processes is a dynamic and rapidly advancing field, in which people with widely varying backgrounds and interests are involved in many different kinds of projects. There are computer scientists who are trying to devise electric "eyes" to read print and also to devise electronic circuits to mimic the coding process in the auditory nerve. An electron microscopist studies the 100,000-diameter magnifications of the receptor cells of the eye to see how light energy may be transformed into the electrical energy of the nervous system. A food technologist in the Army Quartermaster Corps tries to predict the acceptability of various foods on the basis of psychological and nutritional measures. A Navy researcher seeks stimuli which will repel sharks; his friend in the Agriculture Department seeks stimuli which will attract certain insects. Some medically oriented researchers try to understand the combination of eye-muscle and perceptual-retraining factors which could alleviate strabismus (crossed eyes); others experiment with the role of a very thin membrane which separates two fluid spaces in the inner ear—the membrane may be involved in a disease that causes deafness and dizzy spells.

Such a list could be extended to great length. One important thing for the student to realize is that along with the wide variety of approaches to sensory processes goes an equally wide range of degrees of scientific rigor in data and theorizing. In this volume there are discussions of such hard-to-define things as feelings of pleasure as well as of the limits of visual acuity—the latter being measured in a controlled experimental procedure and defined in operational terms (that is, in terms of the particular measurement procedure employed). The reader should keep such differences in mind as he evaluates the statements and theories presented in this volume.

DEFINING THE STIMULUS

With any approach, however, the initial problem is the same: the starting point for the study of sensation is defining the stimulus. The physicists' measurements of particle energies—of photons, protons, and electrons—must be combined with the psychologists' measurements of differences in an organism's behavioral responses to this energy in a controlled testing situation.

Before you can talk about light, you need a human eye; before you can define sound, you need a human ear.

The physicist starts us off with six classes of stimuli: acoustic, photic or electromagnetic, mechanical, thermal, chemical, and electrical. Although the differences in the physical nature of the stimuli require separate experimental methodologies, the basic aspects of stimulus definition remain the same for each. A stimulus is defined in the following terms: (1) the *qualitative* dimension, which includes the electromagnetic wavelengths, vibration frequencies, or chemical substances to which receptor cells will respond. The qualitative dimension also includes perceptions of color, pitch, and the various tastes and smells; (2) the *quantitative* or intensive dimension, which starts with the minimal amount of stimulus energy necessary to evoke a selected behavioral response and then measures changes in psychological intensity as stimulus energy is increased; (3) the *temporal* dimension, or duration; and (4) a *spatial* dimension, which is most applicable to vision and the cutaneous senses.

The student should note the degree to which our knowledge about an individual sensory system is dependent upon the particular difficulties encountered in defining the stimulus. For example, our knowledge of the visual and auditory systems has benefited greatly because stimuli can easily be measured accurately and the subjects can make consistent and similar responses. In comparison, our knowledge of the olfactory system has been retarded by difficulties with measures both of stimuli and of responses.

SENSORY PROCESS AND ONGOING BEHAVIOR

To obtain precise reproducible measurements of sensory stimulus-response relationships, it is generally necessary to simplify experimental procedures and to deal with one sensory modality at a time. However, a principal aim of sensory psychology is to be able to understand these relationships in the full complexity of the life of a normally behaving organism. It is well, then, to keep in mind what an organism confronts as it tries to act sensibly in the midst of a "blooming, buzzing confusion." In human terms: Our behavior is based on responses initiated by the direct contact of objects with our skin and taste receptors, and by energy traveling to our eyes, ears, and nose. All this information about objects and events around us has to be correlated with information from several different types of internal receptors. These are responsive to changes in the position of limbs, movements of our whole body and head, and important aspects of our internal physiology. Thus, due to this correlation between internal and external environments, we can make judgments about the movement of objects even though we are also moving; similarly, our taste sensations may vary as we feel hungry or overstuffed.

It may seem that there is little information about our environment, either internal or external, of which we are unaware. Although our sensory processing probably includes a greater number of differentiations than that of any other single species, there is still much information in the environment to which we are not responsive, and, to some of which, other species are responsive. The pit-viper locates his prey with an infrared detector; bats and porpoises locate theirs with echoes from high-frequency sound pulses which they emit; dogs use their very sensitive noses for following the paths of other animals; bees act as if they can orient their flight through detecting the plane of polarization of sunlight (although this is somewhat controversial); some fishes detect nearby objects by changes in an electrical field with which they surround themselves. This list could go on and on. New mechanisms of sensory processing in different animals are constantly being discovered.

Although we may sometimes wish we could experience the sound of the high-frequency environment and the appearance of the infrared, our sensory limitations are probably blessings. We, as well as other organisms, seem to have only the sensory capacities that are needed for our own particular range of behavior. We do have the capacity to increase our existing sensitivities when this is necessary (the "facial vision" of the blind person and the ability of the wine taster to discriminate the vintage, vineyard, and particular hillside of an unknown sample are notable examples), but to be constantly processing more information would probably only create extra problems for the central nervous system. A large part of the brain's processing of sensory input already seems to involve active filtering and selection. We generally attend only to a small fraction of the available stimulus information—that which is needed for ongoing behavior—and are unaware of the rest. You have probably had the experience of finding yourself cut or bruised with no memory of when it happened. Severe wounding can occur without pain or awareness if a person is busily engaged with something. Another example of a reduction of extraneous and unnecessary sensory input is provided by the sensory filtering process during sleep and the oft-cited responsiveness of a sleeping mother to her baby's crying. Abundant data on neuroanatomical and neuro-physiological inhibitory processes at all levels of the brain's processing of sensory input indicate how this filtering and selection process may take place.

When we consider sensory mechanisms in terms of ongoing behavior and in terms of the total organism, two concepts are important: (1) There is a correlation between species-survival behavior—food getting, mating, and self-protective behavior—and the sensory equipment necessary for efficiently providing the information upon which this behavior depends. (2) In pursuit of a particular behavior sequence, only a limited amount of the total sensory input is utilized. This relationship —between the range of a particular organism's behavior, the organism's sensory equipment, and its sensory-information processing—is well illustrated by the phylogenetic development of sensory systems.

THE PHYLOGENETIC DEVELOPMENT OF SENSORY STRUCTURES

By starting with single-celled organisms, the phylum Protozoa, we clearly see the degree to which behavior may be described in terms of maintaining a necessary range of optimum physiological conditions: temperature, oxygen, pH, energy sources for metabolism, etc.

The amoeba, the simplest of protozoa, has nothing that can be described as a sensory system. Yet it exhibits the wide range of sensitivities necessary for it to maintain optimum physiological conditions, sensitivities quite similar to those provided by a well developed sensory system. An amoeba's behavior is influenced by temperature changes, chemical and mechanical stimuli, light, and gravity. The flowing movements of its pseudopods depend upon the *intensity* of stimulation. If a single mechanical stimulation which is too weak to cause any observable change in pseudopod movement (subthreshold stimulation) is applied several times in succession, a response may be elicited. Such a response is said to be due to *temporal summation*. An amoeba will also *adapt* to a maintained stimulus. For example, a steady intense light first results in a general bodily contraction and quiescent period. In a few minutes, adaptation to this stimulus occurs, and movement is initiated. These three stimulus-response properties of protozoan protoplasm— graded response to stimulus-intensity differences, temporal summation, and adaptation—are quite characteristic of highly developed sensory systems consisting of specialized receptor cells and extensive central-nervous-system processing. Distinguishing the specialized sensory systems of higher organisms from simple protoplasmic sensitivity are greater sensitivity and both a greater speed and a greater variety in stimulus-response relationships.

In the Porifera, the simplest of the multicellular animals, the sponge illustrates further development. Each cell of its water-intake opening (operculum) acts as a receptor and an effector, contracting when stimulated. This action results in a primitive type of transmission of stimulation based on the contraction of one cell pulling on its neighbor and thereby stimulating the neighbor to contract.

True nervous stimulation first occurs in the phylum Coelenterata, which includes hydras and jellyfish. This is the first group of animals to do much moving around. Once an organism starts to swim, it is faced with many more choices and a wider variety of environmental conditions. To meet these increased needs, the hydra's sensory system consists of receptor cells which are more sensitive to mechanical, chemical, and thermal stimuli than are the other cells of the body and which have fiber-like branched extensions which connect to muscle cells. These receptor cells, because they combine both sensory and neural functions, are called neurosensory cells. Hydras and jellyfish also contain a nerve net, which looks like its name and is formed from cells specialized for conduction of neural impulses.

Jellyfish also have receptors sensitive to a single type of stimulation. Within pits around their outer margin are cells responding to chemical changes; the ocelli, also within the pits, are sensitive to light and contain pigmented cells below a lens structure. The animal's upright position is maintained through statocysts, structures containing small dense particles resting on hair-bearing sensory cells that are sensitive to the directional force of gravity and acceleration. This increase, in comparison with lower forms, in the complexity of the sensory-neural system is paralleled by a much wider variety in its behavior.

As we move up the phylogenetic scale, we see important sensory advances in flatworms (phylum Platyhelminthes) and roundworms (Annelida). The advances are primarily a result of the shift in body structure from the radial symmetry of lower organisms to the bilateral symmetry of the worms. This shift affords the opportunity for the development of a head end. An animal with a head end is generally receiving movement-caused stimuli in a regular order and with a set orientation. This is in sharp distinction to the radially symmetrical animals that swim with any part forward. The crucial role of the head is seen in its concentration of specialized sensory organs and the beginnings of a central nervous system—the paired cephalic ganglia. Worms make finer adjustments than lower forms to a greater variety of environmental conditions. The change from the water habitat of many flatworms to the land habitat of many roundworms usually involves a change to a greater range of environments (above and below ground), to rapid changes between environments, and to a greater range of light, temperature, and moisture and ground-surface characteristics. The sensory thesholds of roundworms are generally lower than those of previous organisms, and they show the first beginnings of modifiability of sensory-motor relationships through repetition. All these advances tie up into an interrelated bundle: (1) bilateral symmetry; (2) a head end with sensory organs and a central nervous system—cephalization; (3) the first true neurons with synaptic connections and rapid non-decremental conduction; (4) lowered sensory thresholds; (5) simple conditioning; and (6) a greater environmental variety with its opportunities for a greater variety of behavior.

The next phylum is Mollusca, which includes clams, octopuses, and snails. The chief sensory advances occurring in these organisms are a greater refinement in the receptors, especially the eyes, and a larger cephalic ganglion capable of simple integration of sensory input from different receptors.

The arthropods—including insects, ants, and spiders—with some 400,000 known species, present a fascinating variety of receptor organs geared to their greater complexities of behavior. The arthropods are the first group to have a social organization, as seen in ant and bee colonies. Most of the characteristics of the arthropod sensory system can be attributed to the small size of the arthropods. This small size, in turn, can be attributed to the following sequence: the air of a terrestrial environment does not provide the support that water does; this leads to the need for some type of skeletal support; whereas chordates developed with an internal skeleton, the arthropods developed with an exoskeleton; since shedding or moulting of the exoskeleton is the only way that growth can take place, the average size of arthropods is quite small (Dethier, 1963).

Within this small size, the arthropod sensory system is typically based on a limited number of receptor elements, but with each element's being able to initiate a behavioral chain. This great sensitivity is the result of the receptors being primary sense cells. Instead of stimulating an adjoining neuron through a synaptic connection as earlier receptor cells do, the primary sense cell performs the dual jobs of the transduction of light, sound, etc., into electrical impulses and the transmission of the impulses to the central nervous system.

A similar small number of large fast-conducting fibers make up the motor system. The end result is a sensory-motor system that sacrifices details of information but achieves speed. Thus the need for flyswatters.

The phylum Chordata, with its broad range of classes from fish through amphibians, and reptiles and birds to mammals, contains an equally broad range of sensory equipment and of approaches to processing sensory information. Since most of the specific discussion in the following chapters on vision, hearing, smell, etc., will be based on vertebrates, this group will not be treated here.

It is interesting to look back briefly at the general characteristics of the phylogenetic development of sensory systems. Two main points seem important. First, there is the previously stressed relationship between an organism's behavioral requirements for survival within a particular environment and its sensory equipment. Let us return to the tunicate sea squirt described in our opening lines. In its larval form it swims freely around, finding food and avoiding predators. In its adult stage, its eyes, its ears, and then its brain all degenerate and become useless—while it lives on food that washes into its intestine.

FUNCTIONS OF SENSATION

Although the sea squirt is an unusual example, it does serve to illustrate the degree to which details of anatomy are almost always best understood in terms of their functions. The range of functional demands increase as the sense organs move from a sea environment—where taste and smell are similar, where osmotic relations and temperature are stable, where humidity is meaningless, where distant vision is impossible—to a terrestrial environment, where there are greatly increased needs and opportunities for sensory discrimination. As functional demands increase, there is development of greater sensitivities and finer discriminations and more complex interactions between sensory modalities.

The extent to which specialized sensory mechanisms perform the necessary tasks of an individual species also illustrates the relation of structure and function. Bats do their food gathering at night, catching insects on the wing. Even when flying through a completely dark cave, they manage to avoid hitting obstacles. This remarkable ability depends upon a process called *echolocation* (Griffin, 1958). The bat emits a series of extremely short, high-intensity, frequency-modulated pulses with a carrier frequency between 50 and 90 kilocycles (2–3 octaves above our own upper limit of hearing, saving us much nightime disturbance). Its two ears receive the pulse echo reflected from these objects at slightly different times and in slightly different intensities. It uses these differences to locate insects and cave walls. Its accuracy in this echolocation is of such a high order that we are presently at a loss fully to understand the process.

Another specialized adaptation to a limited, nighttime environment is found in birds that migrate at night. A growing body of evidence indicates that celestial navigation, determining the direction of flight by the stars, is the technique used innately by many of these birds (Sauer, 1960).

The list of specialized sensory mechanisms is another that could be greatly extended. These adaptations are an outcome of thousands of years of evolutionary improvements. They point to the need for analyzing sensory processes in terms of the behavior of an organism.

The second important characteristic of sensory development which is illustrated by the phylogenetic series is that there is a shift from the predominantly invariant relationships between stimulus and response in lower organisms to a greater plasticity and multiple determination of stimulus-response sequences in higher forms. This shift can be largely attributed to the degree to which higher centers in the central nervous system take over the sensory-processing functions previously handled by lower centers. Fishes have pattern vision without having any cerebral cortex; if the cerebral cortex of a cat is removed, a severe deterioration of pattern vision results.

The previous discussions have stressed an information-processing role for sensory systems. Our emphasis has been on the maintenance of ongoing behavior by input—information about the state of both the internal and external environments. This is the traditional role assigned sensory systems—and certainly the most important one.

However, an increasing amount of recent data points to the importance of two other functions for sensory input. First, there is maintenance of the general arousal level of an organism. The neural input from all sensory modalities has two pathways. One, the primary projection, ascends to areas of the cerebral cortex specific to each modality. Along the way, however, branches from each go into a large central core of the brain stem. This area, containing nerve cells responsive to all types of sensory input, is called the brain-stem reticular formation (French, 1960). Through a shifting balance of excitatory and inhibitory activities, the reticular formation maintains different levels of behavioral arousal, varying from the hypersensitive and hyperactive animal to the comatose. Arousal is normally maintained by the amount and novelty of the sensory input to the reticular formation. Some very interesting data of importance to space-flight planning have come from sensory-deprivation experiments in which humans have been isolated in environments that restrict sensory input to a minimum. (Soloman et al., 1961).

The second additional role of sensation is one of pleasure (Pfaffmann, 1960). Much of our cultural, recreational, and sexual activity may be looked at in terms of the sensory gratification it provides. Neurophysiological data or psychological theorizing does not adequately explain the pleasures one gets from listening to a Bach toccata or from walking through a deep silent wood. We don't even have a good vocabulary to describe the pleasurable sensations of the fullback after a perfectly executed 60-yard touchdown run or those arising from a fast swim through heavy ocean surf. Although these are feelings perhaps best described by the poets, there are some recent experimental data on an extensive area of one of the earliest-developing parts of the brain, the limbic system, which point to its role in emotional and motivated behavior and the existence there of separate positive and negative motivational areas (MacLean, 1954; Brady, 1958).

An animal will keep vigorously pressing a bar for long periods when the effect of his pressing is to provide a small electrical stimulation through a fine electrode implanted in one of several portions of the limbic system (Olds, 1966). In many instances, the hungry rat will choose to press a bar for the electrical stimulation rather than press one for food. There are extensive sensory pathways into the limbic system. Its old name, rhinencephalon or "smell brain," was an indication of its intimate connection with this sensory modality, but we now know that all other modalities are also represented there.

SOME LIMITATIONS

Due to the comparative newness of the data and concepts of the arousal function and the pleasures of sensation, there is as yet no satisfactory or simple way of incorporating this material into the traditional problems of hearing, vision, etc. It is important, however, to bear in mind, while learning of the sensory systems' mechanisms for coding particular stimulus variables and for handling the informational content of sensory input, that this is only part of the picture.

The information in the following chapters is derived typically from experiments carried out in the controlled environment of a laboratory, often using anesthetized animal preparations. The simplifying of the stimulus-response situation is a prime consideration in psychophysical procedures. To measure such things as the change in the threshold of a tone when it is paired with another tone requires extensive experimentation in a sound-proof room with many well motivated subjects who have been trained for this specific task. The response made by the subject to indicate the presence of a given sensation is also kept as simple as possible and selected so as to be free of irrelevant and uncontrolled variables.

Only through a process of step-by-step reduction is it possible for researchers to get deeper and deeper, from the psychological down to the molecular relationships of sensory mechanisms. In doing this, it is important for them and for the student to realize that there is no "vision" or "hearing" at the molecular level and that the path back up is a many-branching path. Two different organisms, even though starting with similar eyes, do not see the same things.

REFERENCES

Brady, J. V. The paleocortex and behavioral motivation. In Harlow, H. F., and Woolsey, C. N. (Eds.), *Biological and biochemical bases of behavior*. Madison: University of Wisconsin Press, 1958.

Dethier, V. G.   *The physiology of insect senses.* New York: John Wiley, 1963.

French, J. D.   The reticular formation. In Field, J. (Ed.), *Handbook of physiology*, Vol. II. Washington, D.C.: Amer. Physiol. Society, 1960.

Griffin, D. R.   *Listening in the dark.* New Haven: Yale University Press, 1958, (also in paperback).

MacLean, P. D.   Studies on limbic system ("visceral brain") and their bearing on psychosomatic problems. In Wittkover, E. D., and Cleghorn, R. A. (Eds.), *Recent developments in psychosomatic medicine.* Philadelphia: Lippincott, 1954.

Olds, J.   Self-stimulation of hippocampus in rats. *J. comp. physiol. Psychol.,* 1966, *61,* 353–359.

Pfaffmann, C. The pleasures of sensation. *Psychol. Rev.,* 1960, *67,* 253–268.

Sauer, E. G. F.   Celestial navigation by birds. *Sci. Amer.,* 1960.

Solomon, P., et al.   (Eds.). *Sensory deprivation.* Cambridge: Harvard University Press, 1961.

ADDITIONAL REFERENCES

Cold Spring Harbor Symposia on Quantative Biology.   Vol. XXX. *Sensory receptors,* 1965.

Buddenbrock, W. von.   *The senses.* Ann Arbor: University of Michigan Press (paperback), 1958.

Galanter, E.   Contemporary psychophysics. In *New directions in psychology.* New York : Holt, Rinehart & Winston, 1962.

Granit, R.   *Receptors and sensory perception.* New Haven: Yale University Press (also in paperback), 1955.

Mayer, C. L.   *Sensation: The origin of life.* Yellow Springs: Antioch Press, 1961.

Milne, L., and Milne, M.   *The senses of animals and man.* New York: Atheneum, 1962.

Rosenblith, W. A. (Ed.).   *Sensory communication.* M.I.T. and New York: M.I.T. Press and Wiley, 1961.

Society for Experimental Biology. Symposium XVI,   *Biological receptor mechanisms.* New York: Academic Press, 1962.

VISION

2

Mathew Alpern

INTRODUCTION

Those who study light have agreed to define it as that aspect of radiant energy of which a human observer is aware through the visual sensations which arise from the stimulation of the retina of the eye.[1] Two of the distinguishing characteristics of light included in this definition are: (1) It is radiant energy. (2) It is capable of stimulating the retina of the human eye. We can learn about radiant energy from physics, but to study the functioning of the retina, we must turn to physiology and psychology. Since light is neither purely physical nor purely psychological, we refer to light as a *psychophysical* phenomenon.

Note that our definition includes, for example, neither infrared nor ultraviolet radiation, for they do not cause visual sensations by stimulating the retina. Nor is light involved in the visual sensations that may arise from a sharp blow to the eye or the passage of a weak electric current through the head—neither of these stimuli is a form of radiant energy. To begin to understand vision, we must know something about radiant energy and something about the retina.

RADIANT ENERGY

Radiation is the transfer of energy through free space without any obvious method of transmission. In modern physics, it is necessary to consider this radiant energy both as transverse electromagnetic waves and as extremely small discontinuous particles of energy known as quanta (or photons).

Consider first radiant energy as electromagnetic waves. We find that while there are many different kinds of these waves (light waves, X rays, radio waves, radar, etc.), they all travel through free space at exactly the same velocity, 3×10^{10} cm/sec, or about 186,000 miles a second. If all electromagnetic waves travel through free space with the same velocity, how do the various kinds of waves differ from one another? Each has its own characteristic frequency of vibration or its own wave-

[1] *The Science of Color*, 1953.

13

length (the product of frequency and wavelength giving the velocity). No matter what the source of radiation (sun, radio-wave generator, X-ray tube, radioactive substance), we identify an electromagnetic wave by its frequency (or by its wavelength). We can think of electromagnetic waves as being arranged into a spectrum according to their frequency (or wavelength). In this spectrum, the range of frequencies between the highest and lowest extremes covers over 70 octaves (i.e., the lowest frequency doubled 70 times gives the highest frequency). The entire range of the visible spectrum (light) occupies less than one of these 70 octaves. The wavelength limits of visible light extend from the extreme violet end of the spectrum (wavelength of about 400 mμ [millimicrons] or four-tenths of a thousandth of a millimeter) to the extreme red part of the spectrum (wavelength 750 mμ). Radiations of wavelengths beyond these limits are not visible and thus are not considered to be light.

We use the wave character of radiation in order to describe several aspects of the visual stimulus, but the initial interaction of radiant energy and the retina can be understood only when we consider light energy to be composed of small particles. As we mentioned, we call these discrete bundles of energy quanta. According to the quantum theory, light can exist only as some whole number of quanta. In general, the number of quanta in a single short-duration low-intensity flash of light, under constant viewing conditions, will not be a constant—the variation in the number of quanta exposed in one hundred successive such flashes will follow statistical rules. Thus when we wish to determine the least amount of energy which can be seen under optimal viewing conditions, we are confronted not only by the normal psychological and biological fluctuations in sensitivity of the observer himself, but also by the physical fluctuations in the number of quanta exposed in successive flashes as well. One of the most amazing facts of sensory psychology is that, under optimal conditions, the absorption of a single quantum of light suffices for the excitation of a visual (i.e., photoreceptor) cell.

LUMINOSITY

It has already been pointed out that radiant energy must be visible to be classified as light. But to determine whether or not any form of radiation is visible to the human eye (and the extent to which it is visible), one must perform a psychological experiment. This is necessary before we can say what light is, much less hope to quantify it. What experiment can be done in order to specify that aspect of radiation to be classified as light?

The simplest approach to finding the limits of visibility would be to follow the lead of Sir Isaac Newton, who, in 1666, let bright sunlight strike a small hole cut into one of the drawn shades of the window of his rooms in Trinity College, Cambridge. The "white" light passing through this hole entered a small glass prism. The prism dispersed this light in such a way that an array of colors from red to violet appeared— like a section of a rainbow—on the opposite wall of the room. If we repeat Newton's experiment and examine the spectrum closely, two features of visible radiation become apparent. In the first place, we obtain the extreme limits of visibility defined by the very red light at one end and the violet light at the other. In the second place, within these limits some parts of the spectrum are much more efficacious for exciting the retina than are others. We observe that the ends of the spectrum appear much dimmer than the blue-green light in the middle of the spectrum. This is true even when efforts are made to insure that each narrow band of wavelengths in the spectrum has the same amount of energy (or, alternatively, the same number of quanta).[2] In order to quantify light, it is necessary to quantify this variation of the magnitude of the visual sensation evoked by equal amounts of energy in the different parts of the visible region of the spectrum.

There are a number of ways in which a psychologist could proceed to do this. The most direct way would be to try to make some estimate of "sensory magnitudes" by asking subjects how bright different parts of an equal-energy spectrum appeared to them. Methods for doing this were invented by the blind Belgian physicist Plateau in 1872, but there has never been a really satisfactory measurement of luminosity by this method. Physicists and others who were confronted with the problem of quantifying light in the early part of this century were not satisfied with such estimates, which they considered too variable and susceptible to suggestion, and so they used a different method. They measured the amount of energy that was required for a given wave band to match a standard light in brightness (ignoring differences in hue or saturation[3]).

The results of such measurements are shown in Figure 1. In this figure, the horizontal axis represents the wavelength of the stimulus. The vertical axis shows the sensitivity of the eye to each wave band. The part of the spectrum to which the eye is most sensitive (green light at a wavelength of 555 mμ) is arbitrarily given a sensitivity of 1.00. At

[2] Because the energy of a single quantum is a linearly increasing function of the frequency of its radiation, equal numbers of quanta of different frequencies have different amounts of energy.

[3] The meanings of these words are to be found in Table 1.

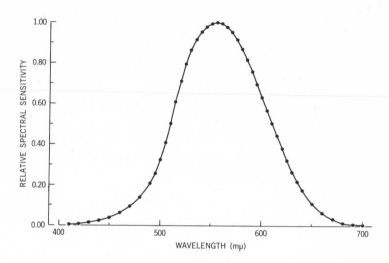

Figure 1

Photopic C.I.E. spectral sensitivity curve. The abscissa scale is in millimicrons; the ordinate in units of sensitivity, relative to the peak value, which is assigned the value of unity.

this wavelength, the observer requires the least amount of energy to produce a brightness match with the standard light. At all other wavelengths, he will require more energy; the ratio of the energy required at 555 mμ to that required at any other wavelength is a measure of the relative spectral sensitivity at that wavelength. The curve is therefore referred to as a relative spectral sensitivity curve—or a luminosity curve. It is one specific example of what the physical chemist calls an "action spectrum." The International Commission of Illumination (in French, *Commission Internationale de l'Eclairage,* or *C.I.E.*) studied the results of careful measurements by scientists in several parts of the world and pooled their measurements to obtain the single curve shown in Figure 1. This curve is identified as the photopic luminosity curve of the C.I.E. standard observer. All photometric quantities—i.e., all units which attempt to assess quantity of light or illumination— must be derived from this curve. Therefore, any photometric unit is a psychophysical measurement that has been derived (directly or indirectly) from the curve in Figure 1. This realization may come as a surprise to those who have used any kind of light meter (because light meters do not seem to involve any subjective or psychological measurement). The spectral sensitivity of the physical receiver in a light meter has been adjusted (i.e., the receiver has been placed behind a suitably colored filter) so that the light meter's sensitivity matches Figure 1 as closely as possible. All other things being equal, the better the match, the better the light meter. Adjusting a light meter is difficult. In fact, it is so difficult to get a perfect match that photometers which involve subjective-brightness matches—made by observers with normal luminosity curves—are usually much more accurate than purely physical detectors.

TRICHROMATIC NATURE OF NORMAL VISION

The experiments which yielded the measurements illustrated in Figure 1 studied one aspect of the response of the retina to light, namely, intensity. Any photoreceptor, whether it belongs to a man, animal, plant, or indeed to inanimate objects—such as a photographic plate or a photoelectric cell—would give such an action spectrum (although the shape of its spectrum might well be quite different). To obtain such a curve, one needs only to be able to vary the intensity of light at a series of wavelengths in the spectrum. Now it has long been known that such a curve does not completely describe every aspect of human vision—normal observers respond to light not only by seeing differences in intensity, but by seeing differences in color, as well.

It is due mainly to the pioneering measurements of the physicist James Clerk Maxwell that we can now make highly quantitative statements about normal color vision in man. Maxwell (1860) mixed colors with a rotating disk upon which sectors of various colored papers could be mounted. As a result of these experiments, and many others that followed along these lines, we can now say that normal color vision is trichromatic. By this we mean that to describe every aspect of color vision, we need at least three unrelated quantitative measurements. To measure every feature of color vision, an instrument must have three independent variables.

It will soon be apparent that what these variables are is to some extent an arbitrary decision of the person who desires to make the color-vision measurements. One common instrument (a colorimeter which stems directly from Maxwell's work) has a knob which varies the amount of red, another which varies the amount of green, and a third which varies the amount of blue in a mixture of lights. With such a device one can quantify quite accurately the normal eye's gamut of color responses to light. This, however, is only one way of doing it, and although it is a very informative method, to which we will return when we go into the problem of normal and abnormal color vision, it is by no means the only one. For the moment, let us look at the matter in a somewhat different way.

HUE, SATURATION, AND BRIGHTNESS

Psychologists find it convenient to keep the terms that describe a stimulus quite separate from those used to describe an observer's response. For convenience, we can designate terms in the first category *psychophysical* and those in the second category *psychological*. The psychophysical term which measures intensity is called *luminance*. The psychological correlate of luminance is *brightness*. All lights, irrespective of other qualities, can be quantified in terms of their luminance. One major effort in sensory psychology is to describe the laws which relate luminance and brightness.

In addition to luminance and brightness, two other aspects of normal vision can be defined. We speak of *dominant wavelength* to designate the psychophysical term which has a psychological correlate of *hue*. The spectrum is composed of light of a large number of different wavelengths, and when they are spread out by a prism, each wavelength gives rise to a somewhat different sensation of hue. For example, light of 700 mμ has a red hue, light of 579 mμ has a yellow hue, light of 500 mμ a blue-green hue, and so on. The normal eye can distinguish a very large number of different wavelengths in the spectrum. A mixture of several different dominant wavelengths in the correct proportion can give rise to a sensation without any distinguishable hue. Such a mixture is called white. In fact, it is possible by proper selection to take only two different dominant wavelengths, and by mixing them in correct proportions, to produce a mixture which looks white. Such pairs of dominant wavelengths are referred to as complements. For example, 609 mμ, which has an orange hue, and 496 mμ, which has a blue-green hue, are a complementary pair; so are 575.5 mμ (yellow) and 474.5 mμ (blue).

The third aspect of normal vision (in the system now being described) relates *purity* (in the psychophysical domain) and *saturation* (in the psychological domain). A pure color is one with little or no white light mixed with a narrow-band monochromatic stimulus; it gives rise to a response of a highly saturated color. A red light (dominant wavelength—say, 650 mμ) in the spectrum produced by a prism is very pure. If a certain amount of white light is added to this, the resulting mixture looks *pink*. The more white light that is added, the more impure is the mixture and—in psychological terms—the more desaturated it appears. The lights in the spectrum are the purest that can be achieved, although some spectrum lights appear more saturated than others. To decide on this last point, psychologists have found that they must add much more white light to some spectrum colors in comparison to others before all traces of hue have disappeared. In this way they have shown that spectrum reds and blues appear much more saturated than spectrum yellows.

Thus, a visual stimulus can be defined in terms of luminance, dominant wavelength, and purity; these correlate with subjective impressions of brightness, hue, and saturation. A stimulus can exist without a detectable dominant wavelength—and thus without any measurable amount of purity. Only luminance will be characteristic of all visual stimuli. Thus luminance is *achromatic,* while the terms "dominant wavelength" and "purity" characterize stimuli which are *chromatic.* These relations are summarized in Table 1.

Table 1

	PSYCHOPHYSICAL (Stimulus world)	PSYCHOLOGICAL (Subjective world)
ACHROMATIC	Luminance	Brightness
CHROMATIC	Dominant wavelength	Hue
	Purity	Saturation

CORRELATION BETWEEN STRUCTURE AND FUNCTION IN VISION

THE EYE

Characteristically, special sense organs are adapted in such a way that the adequate stimulus achieves excitation with a minimal expenditure of energy. This is especially true of the eye of the vertebrate; this eye's sensitivity to light under optimal conditions approaches the theoretical limits of any radiation detector. The reader no doubt already has been exposed to an elementary description of the optics of the eye. An adequate discussion can be found in any elementary college physics or physiology book.

ACCOMMODATION

Optically, the lens system of the human eye is composed of a fixed-focus highly refractive cornea and a variable-focus lens. The lens contributes only about one-third of the total refractive power of the eye. Its major role, however, is to allow the eye to focus on objects at different distances. This automatic focusing is perhaps the most amazing optical feature of the human eye. If we change our gaze from objects at far distances to things close at hand, within a third of a second the near object becomes sharply focused; a shift in the opposite direction is achieved almost as quickly. The changes in optical characteristics which shift the eye's focus are referred to as changes in accommodation. The details of this process are fascinating but beyond our scope here. It is necessary to emphasize only that the lens system in the eye operates much more efficiently than any automatic focusing apparatus yet designed by man.

PHOTOPUPIL MOTILITY

Another automatic adjustment in the optical characteristics of the eye comes about as the intensity level of the visual field changes. The eye sees at an enormous range of light levels. The maximum light level at which vision is still tolerable is some ten thousand million times as intense as the minimum amount of light necessary for vision under fully dark-adapted conditions. There are several different ways in which this enormous range is achieved. Neural and chemical systems which allow the sensitivity of the eye to adjust to the prevailing levels of illuminance will be considered later. They produce the major changes in adaptation to light or darkness. Unfortunately, these retinal adjustments are extremely slow; it takes about 30 minutes to obtain maximum sensitivity in the dark after exposure to a very bright light. To facilitate a more rapid adjustment of sensitivity, the sphincter muscle in the iris contracts when the eye is exposed to light and relaxes when the eye is exposed to darkness. This process produces a change in size of the pupil—the pupil is wide at low light levels and very small at high light levels. In this way we get as much available light as possible to the retina in order to see at twilight, on the one hand, and to minimize the excess intensity of bright daylight, on the other. This adjustment will permit a range of sensitivity of only about 20 to 1 (rather than the 10 billion to 1 which retinal adaptation effects). Nevertheless, the iris begins to contract in only about one-fifth of a second following the onset of the light flash; and, because of this remarkable speed, the adjustment is of considerable importance in the early moments of transition from one light level to another.

In amphibians (such as frogs) and fishes (especially eels), the change in length of the smooth muscle of the iris sphincter is brought about by the absorption of light quanta by a photochemical substance within the muscle itself. This photochemical substance is in fact the very same substance found (in much larger quantities) in the most numerous photosensitive cells within the retina. In other vertebrates, such as cats and man, this function has been lost. In these cases, however, the changes in the length of the iris sphincter can be effectively achieved by stimulation of the retina by light. While the retina in man contains four different kinds of photosensitive cells, it is now known that absorption of light quanta by any one of these can successfully make the iris sphincter muscle contract under optimal conditions. The minimum amount of light necessary to produce a detectable change in the size of the pupil is sometimes 1.2-2.0 times larger than the minimum amount of light necessary for vision, but this slight difference may be nothing more than a reflection of the crudeness of our methods for measuring changes in length of the iris sphincter, compared to the exact way we can measure the minimum energy required for vision. Since the first of these methods is "objective" and the second is "subjective," the student will understand that when a psychologist strives for objectivity in his measurements (which may be a desirable characteristic), he is by no means assured that in the process he will gain greater sensitivity.

THE DUPLEX RETINA

In man and almost all vertebrates, the photosensitive elements of the retina are of two major kinds. The anatomist Max Schultze, in 1866, first noticed the difference between these two kinds of cells and called them *rods* and *cones,* depending only upon whether their outer segments (the parts containing the photosensitive substances) were long, cylindrical filaments or short, stubby, and conical. We assign quite different functions to these basically different structures. Over sixty years ago, Parinaud and, later, Von Kries (quite independently) developed what is now called the *duplicity theory of vision*—a monumental generalization relating structure and function.

According to the duplicity theory, rods and cones are responsible for quite different kinds of vision. Rods are the photoreceptors of night vision; cones, the photoreceptors for day vision. We use rods in order to detect very weak amounts of light. Their responses are achromatic. Their visual acuity—their ability to distinguish one point in space from another nearby point—is very poor. Cones operate at high levels of illumination. Their visual acuity is very high. Our ability to have normal trichromatic color vision depends only upon cones and not at all upon rods.

Rods are most numerous in the peripheral retina and are absent from the very center (the fovea) of the retina. It is the center of the retina that we use to see fine details, and only cones are found here (although they have here a less conspicuous conical shape than elsewhere). In very dim lights, we see only with rods; our peripheral retina is more sensitive to very weak light than is the central retina. The French physicist N. F. J. Arago (1786–1853) first observed that on a very dark night one can see more clearly the distinction between two stars that are very close together by looking to either side of the pair rather than by looking directly at it. The relative insensitivity of the center of the visual field at very low light levels is sometimes referred to as the *Arago phenomenon.*

Rods and cones differ functionally not only in their relative sensitivities to light but in other ways as well. In fact, the difference in sensitivity may be more a matter of nerve connections than of a basic difference in sensitivity between single cones and single rods. It is known that the human retina contains six million cones in comparison to 120 million rods. Now all of these sense cells can relay information to the brain only by way of a mere two million ganglion cells whose axons make up the nerve fibers of the optic nerve. It is at once evident that a single ganglion cell connects—by way of intermediate cells (the bipolar cells)—to very many photoreceptor cells. But because of the requirements of very high visual acuity in the center of the retina, the foveal cones are thought to have more nearly private-line connections to the brain than do the rods and cones of the peripheral retina. For these reasons, there are many more rods connected to bipolar cells which converge on a single ganglion cell than is the case for cones. Hence, spatial summation (the increase in sensitivity to a stimulus light by increase in its size) is much greater for rod vision than for cone vision.

Because of aberrations in the optical components of the eye and of diffraction effects at the pupil, the retinal image of even the smallest possible point of light stimulates several hundred rods and cones. Thus the photosensitivity of a single photoreceptor cannot, with presently available methods, be measured in the intact living eye. However, there is a range in which variation in the size of the stimulus can be computed to produce a variation in the number of photoreceptors stimulated. Within this range, as the stimulus target gets smaller and smaller, the measured rod and cone sensitivities approach each other more and more. Many believe that if the measurement could be made on single rods and single cones, the sensitivities in the two cases would be identical.

SPECTRAL SENSITIVITY

Another way in which rods and cones differ is with respect to their respective responses to variation of the wavelength of light. We must qualify our assertion that normal vision is trichromatic. This is true only for the very center of the visual field and then only at very high levels of illumination. This is to say, normal cone vision is trichromatic. Rod vision, on the other hand, is achromatic. Rods respond to difference in wavelengths only by registering differences in intensity, not differences in hue and saturation.

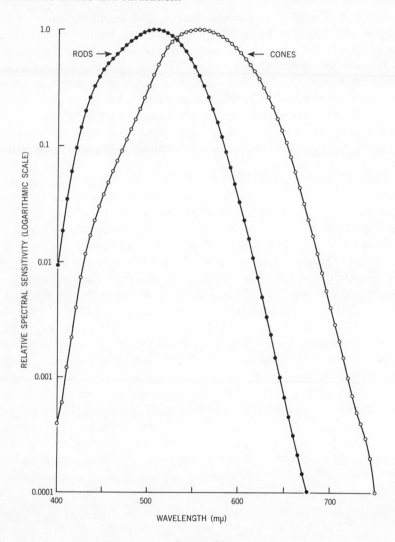

Figure 2

Comparison of the rod and cone relative spectral sensitivity curves. The ordinate for each curve has the value relative to its peak value. The cone curve is plotted from exactly the same data as that in Figure 1, but the ordinate scale is logarithmic rather than linear—note how the logarithmic curve changes shape at the extremes of the spectrum.

Furthermore, the spectral sensitivity of the achromatic rod response differs from that of the cones. Figure 1 was described as representing the spectral sensitivity of the normal human eye. To be more precise, the curve in Figure 1 represents the spectral sensitivity only of the center of the fovea, at moderately high levels of illumination. That is, Figure 1 represents the spectral sensitivity of cone vision. To measure the spectral sensitivity of rod vision, one can determine the weakest amount of energy an observer in a fully dark-adapted state can detect in the peripheral visual field where rod vision is most sensitive. Figure 2 shows the spectral sensitivity of both rods and cones for comparison. The data for the cones are the same as those illustrated in Figure 1, but the ordinate scale in this case is logarithmic while in Figure 1 it is not.

Figure 2 shows that the wavelength of maximum spectral sensitivity for cone vision falls almost 50 mμ toward the red end of the spectrum in comparison to the wavelength of maximum rod sensitivity. The student should not be misled by the fact that the maximum sensitivity for each curve illustrated in Figure 2 has been arbitrarily assigned the same value. This was done to show the *relative* spectral sensitivity of each curve with respect to its maximum; in this case, each was assigned the value of 1. (We have already noted that rod vision, at threshold, is about 1,000 times more sensitive than cone vision).

Although these quantitative relations have become exact only within the last twenty-five years (following development of modern spectrophotometric methods), the Bohemian physiologist J. E. Purkinje, in 1825, observed the change in relative brightness of red and blue flowers as the sun gradually set in twilight. Selecting two such flowers, the colors of which looked equally bright under daylight conditions, he found that at low light levels, the blue appeared brighter than the red, although the chromaticity of each had faded. Thus this shift of the spectral sensitivity of the eye on changing from high light levels (cone vision) to low light levels (rod vision) is frequently referred to as the Purkinje effect.

ADAPTATION

Another way in which rod vision differs from cone vision is in the speed with which the two receptor systems successfully "adapt" to a reduction in the light level. If we look at a bright light for a considerable time and then into total darkness, our sensitivity to light is impaired for a considerable time and only gradually approaches an optimum value. This gradual process is referred to as *dark adaptation*. As was pointed out above (see page 20), the dark-adaptation process ordinarily includes a certain time during which the pupil of the eye is becoming larger. This improves sensitivity, since the wider pupil permits more light to reach the retina. If a psychologist is interested in studying only the changes in retinal sensitivity during dark adaptation, he can make his measurements through a small artificial pupil which is smaller than the smallest possible natural pupils. Alternatively, he can temporarily paralyze the iris muscle so that it is incapable of changing its length and thereby of changing the amount of light reaching the retina. (A relatively harmless drug dropped into the eye temporarily immobilizes the pupil for this purpose.)

A typical dark-adaptation curve would consist of the measurement of the minimum amount of light necessary for vision in the dark at various time intervals following exposure to bright light. An informative curve can be obtained by using a relatively large test target (say 5°) which is exposed in the peripheral visual field about 30° nasally from the point of fixation. Figure 3 illustrates the results of such an experiment, in which changes in pupil size were not permitted to influence

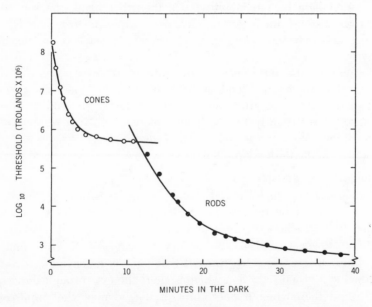

Figure 3

Dark-adaptation curve showing the change in sensitivity of Hecht's right eye after exposure to 400,000 trolands for 2 minutes. The unfilled circles show data for which the violet color of the test flash was clearly visible; the filled circles are data where the test flash appeared colorless. (Data from Hecht, et al., 1937. Reprinted by permission of The Rockefeller University Press.)

the measurements. The subject for this experiment was Selig Hecht (1892–1947), one of the first to show how well some of the attributes of vision can be directly related to physical and chemical events in the retina.

In the figure, the vertical scale shows the logarithm of the test intensity required for visibility, and the horizontal axis shows the variation in time (minutes) in the dark. It is apparent that in the 30 or so minutes in the dark the minimum amount of light required for visibility decreased over 100,000 times. Of particular interest is the fact that dark adaptation is described by two smooth curves rather than by one. By changing the wavelength of the stimulus and the region of the retina tested, it can be proved that the first of these two curves describes changes in the sensitivity of cones and the second describes changes in sensitivity of rods.[4] Such experiments prove that cone sensitivity increases relatively quickly following exposure to very bright light (50% recovery takes only about 90 seconds in the dark, and dark adaptation is complete by ten minutes). On the other hand, the sensitivity of the rods changes much less rapidly. After exposure to a very intense light, the rods may take more than 30 minutes to reach their maximum sensitivity.

Because of the difference in the rate of recovery, the first few minutes following intense light adaptation finds the cones more sensitive than the rods, but after ten or fifteen minutes the rod sensitivity has improved sufficiently that it is now higher than that of the cones. The transition from cone to rod vision is identified by the discontinuity (the "kink") in the dark-adaptation curve.

DIRECTIONAL SENSITIVITY

A final way in which the rods and cones differ is in their directional sensitivity. For a long time, it was believed that no matter from which direction light reached the rods and cones, it was equally effective in excitation. However, in 1933, the British physicist W. S. Stiles and his collaborator, B. H. Crawford, proved that light is much more effective in producing a visual sensation when it enters the eye through the center of the pupil than when it goes through the edge of the pupil, even though the light is stimulating exactly the same photoreceptors in both cases. This can be shown either by subjective-brightness matches between lights going through different parts of the pupil or, in fact, by measuring the effectivity of the light in making the pupil contract while passing through different parts of the pupil. A long extended

---

[4] As we stated, the center of the retina has only cones. When we test that area, we obtain only the first of the two curves describing dark adaptation.

series of experiments have suggested that this result is best explained by the idea that the light which strikes the photoreceptor directly along its axis (presumed directed at the pupil center) is much more effective than the light which strikes the photoreceptor obliquely. While the full explanation is still to be developed, modern ideas about the Stiles-Crawford effect suggest that the photoreceptors act very much like wave guides or dielectric rod antennas. However this may be, the interesting point for our present purpose is that only cones possess directional sensitivity; the rods are equally responsive to light irrespective of the region of the pupil through which it passes.

Our discussion of the duplex retina has emphasized how rods and cones differ in functional and structural characteristics. In many different studies of visual function, particularly in studies in which the level of illuminance is varied from very low to higher values, the duplex character of the retina is demonstrated by two curves—like those in Figure 3—of which one (the low-intensity curve) reflects the response of the rods and the other (the high-intensity curve) reflects the response of cones.

Through measurements in the center of the fovea and then in the peripheral retina, by variation in the wavelength of the stimulus light and in the region of the pupil through which the light passes, it can be very assuredly documented whether a particular curve represents functioning of rods or of cones.

THE CHEMISTRY OF ROD VISION

No questions in sensory psychology are more important than those about the manner in which a sense cell is excited by its adequate stimulus. How do the light quanta cause the excitation of rods and cones? As a point of fact, we know very little which can help to answer this question. What little is known about rod excitation, however, is more explicit than what is known about the excitation of almost any other sense organ.

Experimental evidence suggests that the first step in the process of excitation of the rods is the absorption of a quantum of light by a single molecule of photosensitive chemical substance which is to be found in the outer segment of the rod cell. What is this evidence? Two strikingly similar results from two completely different kinds of experiments, one purely physical chemistry, the other purely psychological.

The first of these experiments involves the measurement of what a chemist calls an absorption spectrum—the amount of light of each wavelength in the spectrum which is absorbed by a solution under study. In this case, the solution contains fragmented particles from the outer segments of retinal rods of a human eye (that has been enucleated for other reasons). The results of this measurement are illustrated in Figure 4. They show that the rod particles absorb light strongly in the region

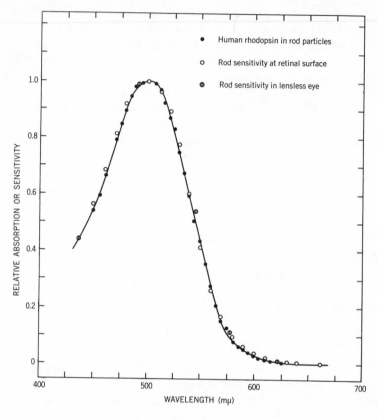

Figure 4

Human rhodopsin and the spectral sensitivity of rod vision. The absorption spectrum of rhodopsin meas-ured in human-rod particles is compared with the rod spectral sensitivity quantized and corrected for absorption in the eye media, as well as with the quantized rod sensitivity of a human eye from which the lens was removed. (Data of Wald and Brown, 1958.)

of 500 mμ (blue-green) but rather weakly at the far ends of the spec-trum.

The psychophysical experiment to which this result must be com-pared has already been described—it is the determination of the spec-tral sensitivity for rod vision, illustrated in Figure 2. To obtain the results in Figure 2 we merely need to measure the minimum energy of light (at the cornea) required for visibility in a region of the visual field where rod vision is most sensitive. To compare the results to an absorption spectrum, two computations need to be made.

The first of these translates the visibility spectrum from an energy basis to a quantum basis. (Light absorption is a quantum phenomenon.) Since the energy of a quantum depends upon its wavelength, the energy required for threshold throughout the spectrum (such as Figure 2) will not yield exactly the same curve as the number of quanta required for threshold for each wavelength in the spectrum. However, a simple calculation allows one to convert from the one kind of spectrum to the other. It is necessary to "quantize" the psychophysical results from Figure 2 in this way before comparing them to the absorption spectrum of rod particles.

A second computation is needed because the energy values which were used to obtain the results in Figure 2 were measured at the cornea whereas light quanta work at the retina. A small amount of light is lost by absorption in the lens. Moreover, the lens is not perfectly neutral but absorbs more blue-green than orange light. We have a reasonable estimate of what this absorption loss is in the lens of a normal observer, but a more exact comparison is achieved by using an observer whose lens has been removed (because of a cataract). The media of his eye absorb a negligible amount of light.

Figure 4 shows the absorption spectrum of rod particles, compared with psychophysical measurements of rod spectral sensitivity curves (1) "quantized" and (2) corrected for losses in the eye media of a normal eye and in an eye without any lens. The agreement of the data is striking. It illustrates the sort of correlation between behavioral data and cellular-level data for which psychologists continually strive.

The data in Figure 4 by themselves do not document our assertion that the first step in the process of excitation in the rod is the absorption of a quantum of light by a single molecule of a photosensitive substance within the rod outer segment. To prove this, we need to know what it is within the outer segment of the rod that causes it to absorb light in the way illustrated in Figure 4.

As it happens, this is not too difficult. One finds that the outer segments of rods contain a large volume (about 30% of the entire rod cell) of a purple chemical substance called *rhodopsin* (or visual purple). By the use of certain detergents it is possible to separate the rhodopsin from the rods and to collect an appreciable quantity of it in a test tube. The absorption spectrum of the rhodopsin turns out to be exactly the same as the absorption spectrum of the rod particles illustrated in Figure 4. There can be no doubt that it is this substance which gives the rod particles their characteristic color and which therefore accounts for the shape of the scotopic (dark-adapted) spectral sensitivity curve.

We have learned a good deal from chemical studies of rhodopsin since its discovery almost 90 years ago. It has a molecular weight of about 32,000. Under the influence of light, rhodopsin changes color (i.e., it bleaches) first from purple to yellow, then to transparency. Unbleached rhodopsin is made up of two kinds of molecules which are linked together. One of these molecules is called the *chromophore* because it is the component which gives the rhodopsin its characteristic color. The chromophore of rhodopsin (and indeed of all known visual pigments) is derived from a special type of Vitamin A which appears to be used for the formation of visual pigments. Ordinary synthetic Vitamin A consists of a long straight chain of carbon atoms with a ring at one end of the chain (so-called *all-trans Vitamin A*). In nature, or after treatment of the synthetic product, Vitamin A can exist in a number of other forms, called *isomers*, in which the originally straight molecule has been bent at one or more different points. It is one of these "bent-molecule" isomers which the retina fits to the surface of the second component of rhodopsin, a special protein called "opsin." The result of this union of the "bent-molecule" derivative of Vitamin A and the opsin is the visual pigment, rhodopsin.

The particular Vitamin A derivative involved is retinaldehyde, which is merely Vitamin A from which two hydrogen atoms have been removed. In its "bent-molecule" form it is called 11-cis retinaldehyde because it is bent around the eleventh carbon atom. So we can describe rhodopsin as 11-cis retinaldehyde linked with opsin.

Apparently the first thing which the absorption of a light quantum does to rhodopsin is to straighten out the 11-cis retinaldehyde into the long straight-chain isomer—i.e., all-trans retinaldehyde. It is this step which apparently triggers the chain of excitatory processes in the rods. The chemical changes which rhodopsin undergoes subsequently probably have little or nothing to do with excitation since they go on either in the light or in darkness. After the all-trans retinaldehyde is produced, it sooner or later becomes detached from the opsin, and this stage is associated with the change in color (or bleaching) from purple to yellow. The further change from yellow to colorless occurs as the all trans-retinaldehyde becomes reduced to all-trans Vitamin A. To reform rhodopsin in the eye, some means must be found to convert the all-trans Vitamin A back into the 11-cis Vitamin A isomer and/or the all-trans retinaldehyde into 11-cis retinaldehyde. Precisely how this is done is still an unsolved problem.

What is the next link in the chain of events which culminates in vision once the light quanta are absorbed by the rhodopsin molecules? We do not know. Any given rod contains a very large number of molecules of rhodopsin. Almost everyone believes that the steps that follow the absorption of light quanta in some way trigger nerve impulses. In the invertebrate (squid) eye, Hagins has been able to trace the flow of local electrical current following excitation with a small point of light in one part of a single rod. A minimum electrical potential was found confined to the illuminated spot and a maximum distributed over the cell body of the illuminated cell. Such experiments suggest that the isomerization of rhodopsin by light is eventually accompanied by a change in membrane permeability of the rod and thus to a flow of extracellular ions (sodium?) in much the same way as a nerve impulse is produced. However this may be, nerve impulses have never been recorded from vertebrate rods (nor cones) nor in fact from the cells with which they synapse. If light absorption does produce excitation by "triggering" the nerve response, one can appreciate a very fundamental difference between photoexcitation which results in vision in animals and photoexcitation which results in photosynthesis in plants. In this latter case, the energy of the absorbed light is itself used to do chemical work—rather than triggering it.

THE CHEMISTRY OF CONE VISION

We know more about the chemical events in the rods than we do about those in the cones. It has been evident for some time that cones contain substances somewhat similar to rhodopsin, but until recently virtually nothing was known about them. There are many reasons for this. Most retinas contain many more rods than cones (in the human eye, the ratio is 20/1); and any given rod contains much more pigment than does a single cone. Thus, isolation of photosensitive material from cones was more difficult and, in fact, has been only recently accomplished. By using the chicken eye (in which a large number of cones are to be found), Wald succeeded in isolating in a test tube a photosensitive material which appeared to be characteristic of cone vision. He called this material *iodopsin* and found that its absorption spectrum maximum is 565 mμ. The test-tube chemistry of iodopsin closely paralleled that of rhodopsin (whose absorption maximum is about 500 mμ). The bleaching by light isomerized the newly discovered pigment in a similar way and its chromophores were identical to those of rhodopsin. Only the proteins (the opsins) differed. Wald named the opsin of rhodopsin *scotopsin* and that of iodopsin *photopsin*.

For a long time it was felt by many that the chemistry of iodopsin and of rhodopsin had nothing at all to do with cone vision in man. But in fact, they are very closely related. To appreciate this fact, we must begin with some very fascinating recent measurements by Rushton at Cambridge. Rushton devised an ingenious method of measuring the characteristics of the pigments in the living human eye. The experimenter shines a pair of colored lights into the eye, one of which will be absorbed strongly by the pigments to be studied; the other colored light is chosen because it will be absorbed little or not at all by this pigment. The light reflected back from the eye is focused upon a photocell, and the relative proportion of the two colored lights reflected from the dark-adapted eye can be measured with fair precision. The eye can then be exposed to a bright bleaching light (which may be white or monochromatic). If this changes the concentration of the pigment under observation, subsequent measurement of the two reflected colored lights will show their relative proportions to be changed. The amount of change is measured by replacing the pigment which has been bleached away by a neutral gray filter in one of the two colored beams. The density of the filter which is needed to restore the dark-adapted proportion of the two colored light beams is a measure of how much pigment was bleached away.

These methods were first used by Rushton to study the characteristics of rhodopsin in the living eye. The validation of the method was achieved largely by comparing these measurements with infor-

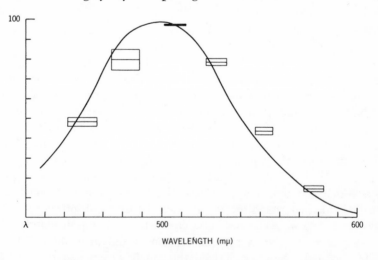

Figure 5

The curve shows the difference spectrum of rhodopsin. Rectangles show the spectrum measured by retinal densitometry. The horizontal dimension gives the wave bands of the measuring light. (Data from Rushton, 1956.)

mation already obtained by indirect methods. For example, Figure 5 shows agreement between the spectrum measured by Rushton, who used different colors to bleach comparable amounts of the pigment, with the spectrum of rhodopsin measured in the test tube. (Rushton's measurements are represented by rectangles.) The agreement, considering the wide difference in methods, is quite satisfactory. In similar ways, by studying the distribution of the amount of rhodopsin in different parts of the retina in comparison to the known distribution of rods in the retina and by a variety of other methods, Rushton was able to prove unequivocally that he was measuring rhodopsin in the living retina.

The value of Rushton's measurements is not limited, however, to what they tell us about rhodopsin in the living retina. By shifting his measuring light from the peripheral part of the retina, where rods numerically are much more predominant, to the fovea, where there are no rods, Rushton succeeded in making very informative measurements of cone pigments in the living retina.

In order to appreciate fully the way these measurements were obtained, it is necessary to digress at this point to say a word or two about color blindness. Color blindness is a problem which has fascinated scientists since its discovery over a century ago. Now, as a result of Rushton's work, we can be quite explicit about it. For the moment, it will suffice to say that there are people we call *protanopes,* who lack the ability to perceive red. They confuse reds and blue greens. Another group of color defectives are called *deuteranopes,* who have reduced ability to perceive green. They also confuse green with purple. Rushton made measurements of the foveal pigments in the cones of normal eyes as well as of protanopes and deuteranopes, but it is easiest to understand his results if we begin with what he found in the color-blind foveas. In the fovea of protanopes he found only a single photosensitive pigment, *chlorolabe* (from Greek, meaning "to catch the green"). The amount of light at various wave bands in the spectrum needed to bleach the same amount of chlorolabe (i.e., its *action spectrum*) agreed very well with the foveal photopic spectral sensitivity (luminosity) curve of the same protanopic observer. In the fovea of deuteranopes, Rushton found one photosensitive pigment. But its action spectrum differs from chlorolabe. It has its maximum absorption in the orange or yellow part of the spectrum. Rushton called this substance *erythrolabe* ("the red catcher"). The action spectrum of erythrolabe not only agrees with the spectral sensitivity (luminosity) curve of the green-defective color-blind fovea but is very similar to the absorption spectrum of iodopsin as measured in the test tube. Some of these relationships will be illustrated in Figure 7.

In the foveas of observers with normal color vision Rushton found both chlorolabe and erythrolabe. His experiments prove conclusively the existence of two photosensitive pigments in the rod-free human fovea. One of these pigments (erythrolabe) was absorbed maximally in the long-wavelength parts of the spectrum, and since it was absent from the fovea of "red-blind" observers, it seems evident that it is the red-sensitive pigment of the normal eye. This appears to be similar (or identical) to iodopsin. Similarly, the other pigment (chlorolabe), present in the protanope's fovea as well as in the normal fovea, is absent from the deuteranope's fovea. It is the green-sensitive pigment of the normal eye.

Rushton's experiments provided the stimulus for a great deal of detailed examination of the monkey and human retina (from eyes removed because of diseases not related to retinal function) by modern methods of microspectrophotometry. This is a method by which the absorption spectrum of a very small number of cells in a living (albeit extracted) retina can be measured. With a microspectrophotometer, Brown and Wald, in the fall of 1963, examined—before and after a fixed bleach—the spectrum of a microscopic field containing about 20 foveal cones. The difference in absorption at each wave band, before and after a fixed bleach, produces a *difference spectrum* of the bleached pigment. Their measurements confirmed Rushton's measurements of chlorolabe and erythrolabe in almost every detail. Furthermore, the experiments provided further evidence that the chemistry of the chlorolabe and erythrolabe was quite the same as that of rhodopsin. By exposing the microscopic field to a very bright light, Brown and Wald could bleach away a large fraction of chlorolabe and erythrolabe in the cones within the field. Which pigment was bleached depended upon the dominant wavelength of the bleaching light. Following such bright light bleaches, the photosensitive pigments could be promptly regenerated merely by adding 11-cis retinaldehyde to the solution bathing the retina. The process could be repeated over and over—as long as enough 11-cis retinaldehyde was present to resynthesize the visual pigments that had been bleached. Erythrolabe and chlorolabe behaved in these circumstances in exactly the same way as rhodopsin. This means that the chromophore (11-cis retinaldehyde) is the same in all three cases. Only the protein part of the molecule (i.e., the opsins) distinguishes chlorolabe from erythrolabe or either of these from rhodopsin. We must assume two different "photopsins," one for erythrolabe, a second for chlorolabe.

While the above experiments provided unequivocal evidence for the existence of one rod pigment (rhodopsin) and two cone pigments (erythrolabe and chlorolabe) in the living retina, there remained two unsolved problems.

(1) In order to explain the trichromatic nature of normal human color vision, it was necessary to identify a third cone pigment. We can give it the name of *cyanolabe* ("the blue catcher"). Rushton's experiments provided no good evidence for cyanolabe, but this was not too surprising. In the first place, color vision for blue is very poor in the very center of the fovea (the fovea is, as we say, *tritanopic*); thus one would expect to find few blue cones there. In the second place, before light reaches the foveal cones, it passes through a yellow (i.e., blue-absorbing) substance (the so-called macular pigment); thus, very little of the blue light which reaches the fovea will be reflected back in comparison to either red or green light. Finally, to make matters worse, tungsten light, which Rushton needs in his apparatus, contains very little blue. These three factors presumably compounded the difficulty of identifying cyanolabe in the normal living retina.

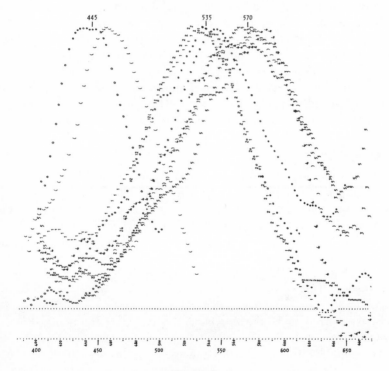

Figure 6

Difference spectra from ten individual primate cones. Curves recorded from monkey cones are represented by numbers, those from human cones by open parenthesis. (Data from Marks, et al., 1964. Copyright 1964 by the American Association for the Advancement of Science.)

(2) The second problem was whether the chlorolabe, erythrolabe, and (presumably) cyanolabe were mixed together in any given foveal cone, or whether each existed individually in separate cones.

Both of these questions were answered simultaneously in the spring of 1964 by further developments of the technique of microspectro-photometry, which permitted measurements of difference spectra in individual cones in the fovea of retinas carefully removed from human and monkey eyes. It was found, indeed, that individual cones contained one (and only one) pigment. Furthermore, individual cones contained *either* erythrolabe *or* chlorolabe *or* a new third pigment, cyanolabe (which was found to have maximum absorption in the blue region of the spectrum, $\lambda_{max} = 450 \text{ m}\mu$).

These measurements, which were made independently and almost simultaneously by Marks, Dobelle, and MacNichol at Johns Hopkins University and by Brown and Wald at Harvard, provide unequivocal evidence at the level of foveal cones for a prediction made over 160 years ago by the English physicist and physician Thomas Young. Young proposed that the retina contained three different classes of "resona-tors" (red, green, and blue) and that these served as the basis of normal trichromatic vision. Figure 6 shows the original data of Marks et al. on ten individual primate cones. The cones from the human are represented by open parenthesis; those from the monkey by numbers.

HOW WE SEE COLORS

The problem of how we see colors is one which has been a sub-ject of almost continual fascination for physiologist and psychologist alike. In the nineteenth and twentieth centuries, the theoretical inter-pretations of color-vision phenomena have been of two distinctly dif-ferent types. The first of these had its origin with Thomas Young and received active experimental support by the work of two famous physi-cists, Helmholtz and Maxwell. It is generally referred to as the *compo-nent* theory. The second theory was developed by Helmholtz's con-temporary and perennial antagonist, the physiologist Ewald Hering. This theory is referred to as the *opponent* theory. As is frequently the case in such theoretical disputes, some facts are better explained by one theory, some by the other. It is therefore necessary to discuss each theory in some detail.

THE COMPONENT THEORY AND THE THINGS IT EXPLAINS

Trichromatism. We have already seen that normal color vision is trichromatic; i.e., that the gamut of the color-vision experiences of the normal eye can be reproduced and measured by manipulation of three independent variables. According to the component theory, this is because the erythrolabe in the red cones, the chlorolabe in the green ones, and the cyanolabe in the blue cones absorb visible light to a greater or lesser extent depending upon wavelength. In the excitation by light of any given wave band, the extent of absorption in each variety of cones varies, and the resulting differential excitation of red, green, and blue cones signals the chromaticity as well as the luminance of the stimulus. Many of the facts of color vision are explained by this idea, including the common types of color blindness. Moreover, the correlation of the absorption spectrum of rhodopsin with the spectral sensitivity of the fully dark-adapted retinal periphery (which we cited as an example of a desirable correlation between behavioral and physicochemical events) has a close parallel in the case of cone visual pigments. What behavioral correlates are there for the absorption spectra of cyanolabe, chlorolabe, and erythrolabe—as measured by Rushton's methods and by microspectrophotometry?

We have already pointed out the close agreement between the absorption spectrum of chlorolabe and the foveal spectral-sensitivity curve of the protanope, and between that of erythrolabe and the foveal spectral-sensitivity curve of the deuteranope.

A similar parallel can be found in the normal eye by adaptation to extremely bright colored lights. Brindley exposed his eye first to a very bright violet light, then to a very bright red one. This treatment rendered him temporarily color blind so that his normal trichromatic color vision became monochromatic; the spectral sensitivity of his eye then was the same as the absorption spectrum of chlorolabe. If the bright adapting lights were first violet and then green, his foveal luminosity curve became very similar to the absorption spectrum of erythrolabe. Under bleaching conditions which inactivated all but the blue cones, a good foveal luminosity curve could not be obtained by Brindley. Fortunately, however, a number of congenitally defective blue-cone monochromats have been described by Blackwell and Blackwell as well as by Alpern, Lee, and Spivey. The blue-cone luminosity curve in these cases agrees very well indeed with the absorption spectrum of cyanolabe (Figure 7).

All of these parallels are a little contrived; none of the behavioral data come from observers with normal color vision who viewed under ordinary conditions of adaptation. Can more suitable parallels be drawn with data obtained from eyes with normal color vision under less severe adaptation constraints? Yes. The affirmative answer stems from some brilliantly simple psychophysical measurements of Stiles. If a small colored test light is superimposed on a bright background, it will not be seen at all (viewed foveally) unless it is of sufficient intensity to exceed what has been called an *increment threshold*. Stiles,

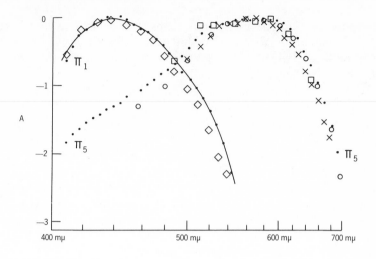

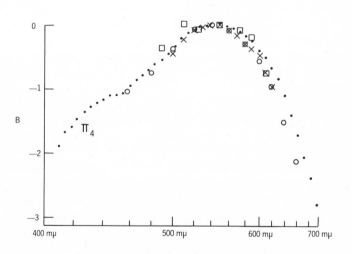

Figure 7

Log spectral sensitivity; curves plotted against wave frequency. A, red and blue mechanisms; B, green mechanisms. Dots represent Stiles' two-color incremental threshold measurements π_1, π_4, π_5. Circles, Wilmer's foveal spectral sensitivity curves in protanopes and deuteranopes. Crosses, Brindley's sensitivities in conditions of artificial monochromacy after adapting to very bright lights. Diamonds, Blackwells' blue sensitivity in blue cone monochromats. Curve, blue sensitivity from spectral matching functions. Squares, action spectra of erythrolabe and chlorolabe. (From Rushton, 1964.)

in a meticulous series of experiments, worked out the relations between the intensity of the test flash at a threshold and the intensity of the background for lights of various wavelengths. He found that the cone increment threshold depended upon three independent color mechanisms with different spectral sensitivities. Stiles called these mechanisms π_1 (blue), π_4 (green), and π_5 (red). Stiles used these terms, because, at the time, he wished to avoid the implication that his color mechanisms were *necessarily* identical to blue, green, and red cones. As it turns out, these mechanisms behave in the same way as the blue, green, and red cones, thus the student will not be far wrong in thinking of them in this way. To determine the action spectrum of the red mechanism, Stiles had merely to determine the number of quanta in the background field at various wave bands in the spectrum needed to raise the red test-flash threshold by a fixed amount. In this way Stiles established spectral sensitivity measurements for π_1, π_4, and π_5 which predict to a very remarkable extent the absorption spectra of cyanolabe, chlorolabe, and erythrolabe, as later measured—first by Rushton on living foveas, then by the Hopkins and Harvard workers with microspectrophotometry—on individual blue, green, and red foveal cones.

Figure 7 shows some of the parallels which we have just discussed. The similarities of spectrum curves obtained by such very diverse means are to be understood as providing the foundation for modern theory of the photoreceptor mechanisms of trichromatic color vision.

Color Blindness. The great majority (over 90% of the male population and over 99% of the female population) possess what we call normal color vision. Any person within this group will match colors and mixtures of colors in a very similar way. However, the rest of the population differ in remarkable ways from the normal group, and it is informative to examine in some detail the ways in which these differences are revealed. The color-defective (a more accurate term than color-blind) group may be subdivided into trichromats, dichromats, and monochromats, depending only upon whether in order to match all colors of the spectrum they require three, two, or only one primary color (Table 2).

Since normal color vision is also trichromatic, we must distinguish between the normal and the anomalous trichromats. While in theory the distinction is clear enough, in fact the borderline is blurred, and the range of trichromatic vision in many ways can be regarded as a continuum, with the normal at one extreme and the extremely anomalous on the other. Normal eyes can match a spectrum yellow by a suitable mixture of a spectrum red and a spectrum green. So can anomalous

Table 2

COLOR BLINDNESS

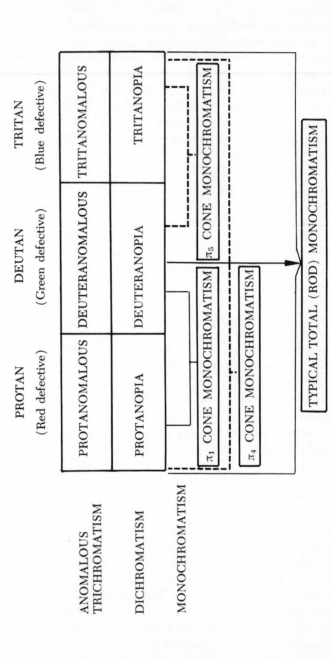

trichromats, but the proportion of red and green in the mixture required in the two cases is quite different. About 5.6% of the male population are anomalous trichromats. Almost all of these (4.6% of the male population) are deuteranomalous. These people will require much more green in a mixture of red and green to match the yellow. (A device which measures the proportion of monochromatic red that must be added to monochromatic green to provide a chromaticity and brightness match with a monochromatic yellow is known as an *anomaloscope*.) Deuteranomalous observers (see Table 2) are probably very deficient in chlorolabe. About 1.0% of the male population is protoanomalous, and they require a very large proportion of red in the red-green mixture to match the yellow in the anomaloscope. Almost certainly protanomalous observers are deficient in erythrolabe. It is still not well understood why protanomalous and deuteranomalous observers set the anomaloscope in their characteristic fashion. Theoretically, a third class of anomalous trichromat, the *tritanomalous* observer, should exist, and he would be characterized by a deficiency of cyanolabe. This condition is extremely rare, and extensive measurements of the color vision of such cases do not exist.

The dichromats can also be divided into three subgroups—*protanopes*, *deuteranopes*, and *tritanopes*—presumably depending upon whether there is the absence of erythrolabe, chlorolabe, or cyanolabe in the retinal cones. It has already been pointed out (page 35) that the center of the normal fovea is tritanopic. When this was discovered, the color-vision characteristics of tritanopia could be studied in enough detail so that a test chart designed to detect tritanopia could be made. A figure made from a series of dots of one color was placed in a background of dots of another color. This background was detectably different from the figure to the normal eye. But the tritanope could see no difference between the figure and the background, and so he saw the chart as homogeneous (i.e., without any figure at all). This chart (called a *pseudo-isochromatic* chart) was run in full color on the cover of an extremely popular British magazine, *Picture Post*. In this way, seventeen confirmed cases were uncovered and seven of these were extensively studied. From the known circulation of the magazine, it can be estimated that the incidence (in Great Britain) of tritanopia is 1 person in 13,000 to 1 person in 65,000. The ratio of men to women in this entity is 1.6 to 1.

Protanopes and deuteranopes, on the other hand, represent respectively about 1.2% and 1.4% of the male population. Protanomaly, deuteranomaly, protanopia, and deuteranopia are all inherited diseases transmitted by a sex-linked recessive mode of inheritance. This is why the incidence is so much higher in the male than in the female population.

Anomalous trichromats and dichromats usually have no further visual disturbances other than their defective color vision. The most reasonable explanation is that the number of cones in such retinas differs not at all from that in the normal trichromat's retina, but there is an anomalous distribution of photosensitive pigments within these cones. (For example, in the case of the protanope, it seems likely that all of the erythrolate in the π_5 cones has been replaced by chlorolabe).

What color does the red- or green-defective dichromat (whether protanope or deuteranope) see in the red-green range of the spectrum? Ordinarily such a question would lie outside the range of laboratory analysis, because the color-vision experience of each individual is unique for him and cannot easily be communicated, except by methods (such as color naming) which are readily subject to cultural and psychological distortions. However, this obstacle was circumvented in a very interesting observer, who had normal color vision in one eye and was dichromatic (deuteranopic) in the other eye. Graham and associates had this observer make a binocular color match between various spectral colors (seen by the deuteranopic eye) with a spectrum (seen by the normal eye). It was found that a spectrum yellow (about 570 mμ) seen by the normal eye matched any wavelength from 515 mμ (green) to 700 mμ (red) exposed to the deuteranopic eye. According to theory, the deuteranopic eye has its normally green-sensitive cones filled with erythrolabe (not chlorolabe as is normal). The red-sensitive cones also have erythrolabe, so they do not differ from the red cones of the normal eye. Now, as Figure 7 shows, both these pigments are sensitive to a greater or lesser extent to a broad band of wavelengths in the red-green range. In the normal eye, if the dominant wavelength is in the red part of the spectrum, the erythrolabe absorbs more light than the chlorolabe, the red cones are therefore more strongly excited, and this is communicated to the brain, which interprets the signal as a red stimulus. If the dominant wavelength is in the green part of the spectrum, the chlorolabe in the green cones absorbs more light than the erythrolabe in the red cones, and the brain interprets the signals which are thereby communicated to it as a green stimulus. In the normal eye, if a yellow stimulus is presented, the chlorolabe in the green cones absorbs the same as the erythrolabe in the red cones, both the red and the green cones are equally excited, and the resulting signals communicated to the brain are interpreted as a yellow stimulus. In the deuteranope, both the red cones and the green cones are filled with the same pigment (erythrolabe) and, to the extent that the pigment absorbs light at all, any wavelength from the red to the green part of the spectrum will always excite the red and green cones equally. Thus the deuteranope (like the normal observer) interprets equal excitation of red and green cones as a yellow stimulus, but for the deuteranope excitation by any wavelength in the red-green range produces this equal excitation and is seen as yellow.

Monochromats have no color vision. To them the pictures in technicolor movies, or color TV, appear exactly the same as the black-and-white pictures do. There are two distinctly different types of monochromats: those very rare cases who have perfectly normal foveal visual acuity, and those who have such poor visual acuity that there can be little doubt that the number of functioning cones in such retinas is greatly reduced. In the former case, it is likely that the disturbances in color vision are not due to difficulties at the photoreceptor level at all, and they are not included in Table 2; so far, they have not told us much of value for color theory. All of the monochromats with poor vision differ from the other kinds of color defectives in that they seem to show an actual deficiency in the number and variety of cones in their retinas. Among this group there is some evidence for four subgroups. Two of these (the total monochromats and the π_1, or blue-cone, monochromats) have been clearly documented, and we can guess that π_4 (green) and π_5 (red) monochromats may be discovered some day. In these latter cases we have dotted them in Table 2. Typical total (rod) monochromats have poor visual acuity and show many signs characteristic of pure rod vision including, besides the low central visual acuity, complete absence of color vision, scotopic spectral sensitivity, reduced flicker discrimination, nystagmus (i.e., rapid to-and-fro movement of the eyes), discomfort at very high levels of illumination, quite satisfactory or superb visual performance in low levels of illumination.

THE OPPONENT THEORY AND THE THINGS THAT IT EXPLAINS

The interpretation of color vision which has been emphasized so far in this chapter has been that elucidated clearly by Thomas Young in 1801 and given wide support by the experimental and theoretical treatments of the German natural philosopher Herman L. F. von Helmholtz some fifty years later. A variety of other color-vision phenomena have been classically explained by the "opponent theory" of Hering. While a critical discussion of the details of the modern version of these two diametrically opposed ideas is beyond the scope of this book, Hering's idea differs from Helmholtz' in that he imagined color-vision mechanisms as basically antagonistic to each other. Young and Helmholtz visualized these independent color systems as supplementing one another. In the Hering view, white and black, red and green, blue and yellow are three paired opposing color systems. Each member of the pair is antagonistic to the other. Thus, the building up of a red sensation, say, is correlated with the breakdown in the green, or vice versa.

If we stare at a bright red light and then shift our gaze to a white wall, the afterimage of the light appears green. This is known as successive contrast or temporal induction. If we look at a gray square on a black background, it looks brighter than a gray square on a white background; a gray square on, say, a red background, takes on a greenish hue. These effects are called simultaneous contrast or spatial induction. The case of a gray square on a white background is called *simultaneous brightness contrast;* on the red background, the induced color effect is called *simultaneous color contrast.*

Induction effects are very easily explained by opponent color-vision theory. The breakdown of the red under prolonged viewing of a predominantly red stimulus depletes the activity of the red system so that spatial or temporal exposure to a neutral (gray) stimulus causes the red opponent (green) to predominate. The phenomenon of simultaneous brightness contrast was viewed by Hering as a consequence of a physiological inhibitory interaction between adjacent nerve cells in the retina. Thus, the electrophysiological activity of the nerve cells excited by the light from the gray stimulus was greatly depressed by stimulation of surrounding nerve cells by the background light. Lateral nerve connections between adjacent retinal areas are a prominent histological feature of almost every vertebrate retina, so that the anatomical connections required by the Hering theory of simultaneous brightness contrast are clearly present.

Helmholtz dismissed the phenomenon of simultaneous brightness contrast as an "error of judgment," implying that physiological explanation was neither necessary nor possible. Modern electrophysiological experiments, however, have provided an abundance of evidence for precisely the kind of interaction effects required not only by Hering's theory of brightness contrast but by his color theory as well. Figure 8 illustrates evidence obtained from a very primitive invertebrate eye (the lateral eye of the horseshoe crab *limulus polyphemus*) showing the lateral inhibition in single visual cells. These experiments carried on by Hartline and his colleagues show that, in a nerve cell, the frequency of firing evoked by a light stimulus is greatly reduced when an adjacent cell is illuminated with a second stimulus. Note also that each cell fires at a lower frequency when its neighbor is illuminated than when it alone is illuminated. This effect is readily eliminated by severing the nerve connections between the cells involved. No one working with eyes similar to our own has obtained elegant quantification of the magnitude that Hartline obtained in this invertebrate. However, qualitatively similar results have been demonstrated on a variety of vertebrates' eyes including frogs' and cats'. There is little doubt that the sort of lateral inhibition illustrated in Figure 8 is more or less characteristic of all eyes (vertebrate and invertebrate). It provides an example of exactly the kind of processes Hering conceived in his theory

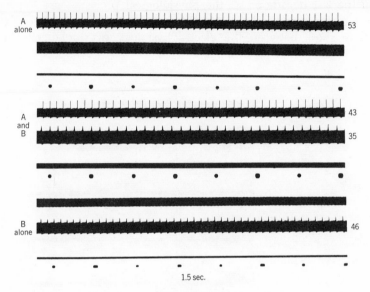

Figure 8

Oscillograms of action potentials recorded simulta- neously from two optic nerve fibers of a lateral eye of a horseshoe crab (limulus) *showing the discharge of nerve impulses when two adjacent visual cells (ommatidia) in which these fibers originate were illu- minated singly and then together. In the top record, one ommatidium (A) was illuminated by itself at an intensity which elicited the discharge of 53 impulses in 1.5 seconds. In the bottom record, the other om- matidium (B) was illuminated by itself at an intensity which elicited 46 impulses in the same period. In the middle record, both ommatidia were illuminated to- gether, each at the same intensity as before; omma- tidium (A) discharged only 43 impulses, ommatidium (B) discharged only 35 impulses in the 1.5 second period. (From Hartline and Ratliff, 1957. Reprinted by permission of The Rockefeller University Press. The photograph here reproduced from printed half- tone copy inevitably shows a loss of detail, and the quality of the results is not representative of the original.)*

of contrasts, many years before it was possible to record the action potential in a single nerve fiber.

Prior to about 1950, a standard criticism of opponent-color-vision schemes was that one could not conceive of reasonable physiological models whereby such opponent effects might be achieved. With the explosion of the developments in microelectrode technology achieved within the last decade or so, the physiological processes are much better understood now, and the surprising result is the very close correlation they show between the electrophysiology of single cells in the

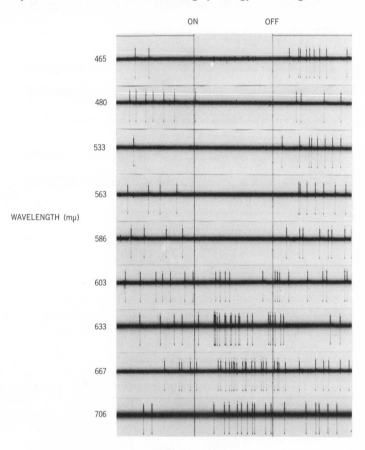

Figure 9

Responses recorded by a microelectrode inside a single cell of the lateral-geniculate nucleus of the monkey. Each record is the response recorded to a light of a different wavelength but of the same amount of energy. (Unpublished data of R. L. De Valois.)

visual system and the theoretically expected results predicted from behavioral (i.e., psychological) experiments.

Look at the curves in Figure 9. They show measurements obtained by De Valois and his associates, who inserted a microelectrode very near to a single nerve cell in the monkey lateral geniculate nucleus. This is the major (thalamic) way station of the nerve pathway that runs from the eye to the higher visual centers of the brain. In Figure 9, the series of records—one above the other—all represent the nerve impulses recorded when lights of the same amount of energy but of different dominant wavelengths are flashed to the eye. The stimulus artifacts at the top of the record indicate the moments when the light went on and off. The important point illustrated in the figure is that the pattern of response to the light very much depends upon the wavelength of the stimulus. For red light (wavelength 633 mμ), there is a very vigorous increase of the rate of firing all of the time the light is on, and an inhibition of firing when the light goes off. On the other hand, green light (wavelength 533 mμ) shows the exact opposite behavior—inhibition of firing all the time the light is on, increased rate of firing when the light is turned off. Intermediate wavelengths show intermediate responses. This essential antagonism between the response of the same cell to red and green light is exactly the sort of physiological opponent process needed by Hering's theory of color vision. Similar antagonistic pairs have been found for yellow and blue lights.

The cell responses like those illustrated in this figure are enormously influenced by the prior light adaptation of the retina. After a very bright green light is used to bleach the retina, the characteristic response of the retina to red light will be obtained by excitation with a much wider range of spectral stimuli than before such bleaching. By analyzing the characteristics of the responses before and after bleaching of the retina by bright colored lights, De Valois was able to infer the nature of the photosensitive material bleached by the adaptation light. The spectral-sensitivity curves obtained from a variety of experiments of this kind clearly resemble those of chlorolabe and erythrolabe (cyanolabe—the blue pigment—is as difficult to isolate by this method as it is by retinal densitometry). This suggests that color-vision systems in the monkey used by De Valois are not really different from those of man.

Because of the basic antagonism between virtually complementary spectrum wavelengths, it is sometimes found that a cell which responds vigorously to excitation of the retina by monochromatic light responds little or not at all to white light (a mixture of a variety of monochromatic lights). However, white light can evoke the response of such a cell—a response very similar to or identical with the response to a monochromatic green—if the exposure of the white light to the cell is made simultaneously with the exposure of a red light to the surrounding area of the retina. Here is an exact physiological duplication at the cellular level of the behavioral phenomenon, color contrast.

If an experimenter studied this cell without any method of stimulating it with monochromatic light he would be puzzled as to what importance such a cell could play in vision, since it remains more or less impervious when ordinary (white) light is exposed to it. By asking the correct question of this cell, however, the experimenter learns a number of powerful things about the color-vision characteristics of the animal at the level of a single cell.

PRESENT STATUS OF COLOR-VISION THEORY

In assessing the present status of color-vision theory, one is led to the conclusion that there is unequivocal evidence, at the cellular level, for the operation of both component and opponent color-vision systems in a single animal. At the level of the receptors themselves, there can be little doubt that the component three-receptor scheme seems to operate in much the way that Thomas Young imagined it to over one hundred and sixty years ago. This accounts for the basic trichromatic nature of normal color vision, the processes and the laws of the color mixing of lights, and the varieties of congenitally defective color vision. Higher in the visual nervous system, opponent processes clearly make a contribution; they account for many of the facts of spatial and temporal induction. The details of this synthesis of thesis and antithesis, and the relative importance of each scheme at successive levels in the visual nervous system, remains the essential problem still to be solved in modern color-vision theory. How do the opponent processes evolve from component inputs? We do not know. However, it seems very likely that physiological processes, such as lateral inhibition, are going to play a key role in the future synthesis of color-vision schemes. For example, very recent experiments suggest that in spatial induction experiments, there is a strong tendency for the individual component systems in one region of the retina to interact (presumably by some process of lateral inhibition) only with the same component system in an adjacent region. Thus, red cones only inhibit red cones, never green or blue ones, while green cones inhibit only green cones, never red or blue ones, and so on. In this view, a gray square on a red background appears blue-green because the red cones from the background tend to inhibit differentially only the red cones excited by the gray square. The uninhibited blue and green cones excited by the square give it an obvious blue-green hue.

DARK ADAPTATION

The curve in Figure 3 illustrates how the sensitivity of the eye improves in the dark after exposure to very bright light. What is responsible for the enormous increase in sensitivity during dark adaptation? A rather old idea is that this merely reflects the amount of unbleached photosensitive substances in the rods and cones. A bright light bleaches the rhodopsin, say, away, and as the rhodopsin slowly regenerates in the dark, the sensitivity of the rods gets better and better. If this were the case, it might be expected that a light which bleaches 50% of rhodopsin in the rods would elevate the rod threshold only by a factor of 2. When it became possible to measure the concentration of rhodopsin in the living eye, it was soon found, on the contrary, that a light which bleached a mere 8% of the rhodopsin sufficed to elevate the rod threshold more than one hundred times. Thus, if a relation between the intensity of light needed for threshold during dark adaptation on the one hand, and the concentration of unbleached rhodopsin in the rod on the other, existed at all, it was clearly not just a simple proportional relationship. To meet this objection, Wald, in 1954, proposed that in the rod (or cone) the molecules of rhodopsin (or of cone pigments) were grouped together in compartments, each of which discharges in all-or-none fashion upon absorption of its first quantum of light. Thereafter, the remaining rhodopsin molecules in this compartment will absorb more quanta from time to time, and those that have already been bleached will also regenerate. But this compartment will not discharge to a stimulus flash until all the rhodopsin molecules of the compartment have been regenerated. Thus the threshold in intensity should increase by a factor of 2, not when 50% of the rhodopsin in the rods has been bleached, but after half of the compartments have been inactivated.

The percentage of the total number of compartments inactivated by very weak adapting lights will be much higher than the percentage of rhodopsin molecules that will be bleached. In fact, provided the amount of bleaching is small, the theory predicts a linear relation between the logarithm of the intensity of light needed for threshold and the amount of bleached rhodopsin. The simplicity of this theory provoked considerable interest when it became possible to put this prediction to exact quantitative test.

Figure 3 shows that during the first ten minutes or so of dark adaptation following a bright bleach, the cone threshold determines the dark-adaptation curve. Consequently, the first rod threshold measurement that can be made is obtained only after about 11 minutes in the dark. Rhodopsin densitometry reveals that at this moment the concentration of rhodopsin in the rods is already about 92% regenerated. Due to the crudeness of the measurements, it is difficult to establish a quantitative relation between the amount of rhodopsin still unregenerated and the intensity of light needed for threshold. However, Rushton (1961) made measurements in the part of the retina of a typical total (rod) monochromat (Table 2) in which there were few, if any, functioning cones but a normal amount of functioning rods. He found that the rod part of the dark-adaptation curve was in evidence from almost the very first moment in the dark. Since the single dark-adaptation curves are exponential functions, the rod-threshold intensity in the dark following a bright light bleach varied over almost ten million times in the rod monochromat instead of the one hundred to one thousand times which can be measured in eyes with normally functioning cones. Rushton studied this patient in two ways: (1) He measured the dark adaptation curve in the usual psychophysical fashion. (2) He measured

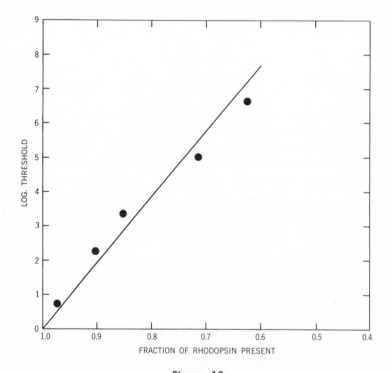

Figure 10

Relation between logarithm of the threshold of the rods during dark adaptation (following a bright light bleach) and the fraction of rhodopsin remaining in the eye of a rod monochromat. (From Rushton, 1961.)

the regeneration of rhodopsin in the same region of the retina by rhodopsin densitometry (i.e., the same method used to obtain the data in Figure 5). The results are illustrated in Figure 10. It is seen that there is a linear relation between the fraction of rhodopsin present and the logarithm of the threshold light intensity, precisely as Wald predicted in 1954 with his compartment hypothesis.

This linear relation between logarithm of the threshold and the fraction of unbleached visual pigment can be demonstrated in other kinds of experiments as well. For example, with foveal-retinal densitometry one can show the same result by observing the changes in erythrolabe (or chlorolabe) at various intervals in the dark following a full bleach, and then by measuring the psychophysical foveal dark-adaptation curve following a similar bleach with red (or green) test light. If one works on rats, the amount of regenerated rhodopsin at various time intervals in the dark following a full bleach can be assayed by sacrificing the animal at the appropriate moment and measuring how much rhodopsin is to be found in the eye. In this case, one also studies a control group of animals which are not sacrificed but whose ability to see following the bleach is measured by the electrical response obtained from the retina when a flash is exposed to the eye. One can do this on anesthetized animals by placing one electrode on the cornea of the eye and an indifferent electrode elsewhere in the body. The voltage generated by a constant test flash is found to greatly increase as the rhodopsin is regenerated. Dowling and Wald (1960) found that there was a linear relation between the logarithm of the flash intensity required to produce a constant voltage at any given time interval in the dark following a full rhodopsin bleach, and the concentration of regenerated rhodopsin at that same moment in the dark.

This elegance in the predictive power of the compartment hypothesis might have led to a premature and unwarranted acceptance of the idea. However, it was evident almost from the beginning that it must be wrong. The logarithmic relation is a prediction for only small bleaches, but the bleaches actually used in such experiments were very large indeed. For large bleaches, the linear-log relation is not predicted by the compartment hypothesis. Furthermore, experiments using different degrees of bleaching and attempting to predict with the compartment hypothesis the threshold changes to a subsequent test flash gave results which were off by a factor of 10^7. But the matter is deeper than only quantitative disparity. It is found, for example, when one varies the size of the test patch used to measure the dark-adaptation curve, that the shape of the curve (both the rate at which it approaches the fully dark-adapted value and this value itself) depends upon the size of the test patch. Now since even the smallest test patch which can be used must excite several hundred rods, it should be immediately apparent that such differences in the form of the dark-adaptation curve cannot be attributed to photochemical and physical events which are only operating within the rods themselves. In fact, it is necessary to assume that it is the nervous connections of the rods which play an important role in the variation of the threshold intensity during dark adaptation. Rushton and Westheimer proved that this was the case by bleaching the retina not with a uniform field but with a grating consisting of alternate light and dark bars (0.5° wide). Now since the rhodopsin in the rods that were exposed to the black bars during such a bleach underwent only trivial amounts of photo-decomposition, if the change in threshold during dark adaptation were uniquely determined by the amount of unregenerated rhodopsin within them, these rods should have shown very little if any elevation of their threshold following the bright light bleach of their neighbors. In fact, Rushton and Westheimer found that the threshold in the (virtually) unbleached rods was elevated exactly the same amount as the threshold in their fully bleached neighbors, and the recovery of dark adaptation in the two cases followed the identical curve. Apparently both the bleached and unbleached rods converge to a common destination, a "summation" pool. It is the state of excitation of its pool, rather than that of the individual rod, which determines the threshold intensity for stimulation of that rod at any moment during dark adaptation. But as Figure 10 shows, the excitation state of the pool (as measured by the threshold) is very clearly related to the amount of unregenerated rhodopsin in at least some of the rods which contribute to the pool. Thus, in darkness, there must be continuous signals from every rod to inform its pool about the number of unregenerated rhodopsin molecules within it. What is the nature of these signals? Why are they not seen? How do they contribute to the elevation of the threshold of the pool? Questions such as these illustrate the unsolved problems of modern theory of dark adaptation. One recent idea is that the threshold during dark adaptation is nothing more than the increment threshold against the background of the afterimage produced by the bleaching light. The signals from the unregenerated rhodopsin molecules in the rods which determine the excitation state of the pool are visible as the afterimage in total darkness. They elevate the threshold not by inactivating the rods but by increasing the "noise" (i.e., the spontaneous activity of all of the cells in total darkness) from which the signal must be differentiated in order to be detected.

DETECTION OF TEMPORAL FLUCTUATIONS OF LIGHT

The response of a photoreceptor to intermittent light characteristically varies depending upon how frequently the photoreceptor is excited. If the rate of periodic fluctuation in the exposure of the stimulus is slow, discrete flashes are easily detected, but as the rate increases, the responses to successive flashes merge. Human observers then describe the effect as "flicker." On further increase, this effect disappears and the physically fluctuating light appears steady. An exact brightness match can then be made between this subjectively steady light and an objectively steady light, if the former has exactly the same total amount of light, i.e. intensity $\times$ duration of exposure) as the latter. Here is a specific example: if a light is steadily flashed on and off in darkness so that it is exposed to the retina 50% of the time, it will exactly match a continuously exposed field whose light intensity is 50% of the intensity of the light phase of the flash. This is known as the Talbot Plateau Law.

The borderline frequency between subjectively flickering and subjectively steady light is known as the critical flicker frequency or critical fusion frequency, abbreviated c.f.f. The c.f.f. is a function of a large number of different characteristics of the stimulus as well as of the characteristics of the perceiving organism. Some of the former include not only the intensity, wavelength, size, and position of the flashing light but its surroundings as well. More complex physiological and psychological factors also play a role. For example, the c.f.f. varies during dark adaptation or as a function of prior light adaptation. Adapting to a light which is alternating above the c.f.f. will elevate the c.f.f., even though looking at a steady light of the same average brightness will not. This means that the organism can, in fact, detect the difference between two lights, one steady and the other flashing above the c.f.f., even though they appear in every way identical. Therefore, the fusion of intermittent light cannot be explained merely in terms of the kinetics of light and dark responses of the photochemical substances in the rods and cones, as has been occasionally proposed.

Other factors which have been reported to influence the c.f.f. include the size of the pupil, body temperature, age (perhaps because the pupil gets smaller and smaller with increasing age), drugs (including alcohol), topical eserine applied to the outside of the eye, inhalation of various gases (including oxygen and carbon dioxide), rapid breathing, "fatigue," and intelligence quotient, among many others.

Most of the important early work on flicker perception was carried out by the examination of the c.f.f. when the flashes consisted of rectangular pulses exposed during half of the cycle. Recently, however, by adapting techniques from electrical engineers, investigators have examined c.f.f. using sine-wave fluctuations in light intensity. With this form of stimulus (Figure 11), it is possible at any given frequency to hold the average intensity (I) constant and merely vary the amplitude of the sine wave (this is what is meant by the so-called percent modu-

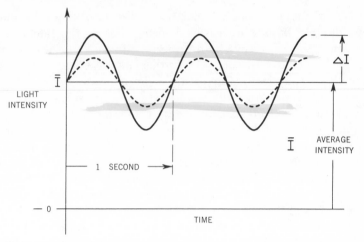

Figure 11

Showing the time variation in light intensity for a sine-wave light stimulus fluctuating at a frequency of 1 cycle per second. If the fluctuations shown by the dotted line appear steady while those shown by the solid line were just perceptibly flickering, then the threshold percentage modulation at 1 cps is $100 \triangle I/I$.

lation), as for example, from a straight horizontal line to the very small-amplitude sine wave, represented by the dotted line, to a pronounced modulation (solid line). In this way, one can measure the minimum percent modulation for perceptible flicker 100 ($\triangle I/I$). This can be done by varying such parameters as frequency, intensity, wavelength, etc., of the stimulus. Figure 12 shows (on a double logarithmic scale) measurements made for relatively monochromatic (orange) light for central fixation and for a moderate size of field. Increasing the luminance of the light shifts curves of this sort slightly to the right and down, but this is true only until an upper limit of average stimulus intensity has been achieved. Average stimulus intensities higher than this limit produce no further displacement of the curve. Conversely, decreasing the luminance (or maintaining luminance constant and shifting the target to the peripheral field) will shift the curve up and to the left and cause some flattening of the low-frequency part of the graph.

It is of some interest that the eye is most sensitive to time fluctuations in the light stimulus in the neighborhood of 10 cycles per second. At this frequency, modulations smaller than 3% show detectable flicker. For higher or lower frequencies, the threshold increases; and in

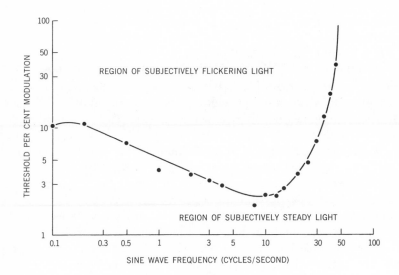

Figure 12

Threshold percent modulation (ordinate) for sine-wave flickering lights of various frequencies (abscissa) scale. Both scales are logarithmic. This observer is most sensitive to about 10 cps flicker at this intensity.

this case, beyond 50 cps, even 100% modulated sine waves go undetected. Under optimal conditions, a 100% cutoff can reach as high as 65 cps, for some observers. The significance of the unusual sensitivity for flickering lights at 10 cps is very poorly understood. There are from time to time theoretical attempts to relate the minimum of the curve in Figure 12 to the well-known fact that the alpha rhythm of the human electroencephalogram has about this same frequency, but so far such theories have not fulfilled their early promise. It seems likely that a better understanding of this sensitivity to 10 cps flicker will come once we know more about the factors contributing to the results obtained at the very high frequencies and at the very low frequencies as well. Much current research of sensory psychologists on the problems of flicker perception is devoted to answering these kinds of questions.

VISUAL ACUITY

Let us now consider the eye's ability to discriminate between very small differences in the spatial position of objects in the visual field. In the nineteenth century, this was a practical problem for experimental astronomy; most of the early measurements of visual acuity were made by astronomers.

It is possible to ask questions about spatial detectability in a number of different ways. One can, for example, gradually increase the width of a very narrow black bar on a white background until it is just visible. It is not just the width of the bar but also how far away it is, that determines whether or not it is seen. This threshold angular width (in minutes[5] of arc at the eye) is called the minimal *visible* threshold. The reciprocal[6] of the minimum visible width is referred to as *visibility acuity*. The minimum angle between two points of light (seen against a black background) which allows the lights to be perceived as double is the minimum *separable* threshold. Its reciprocal is known as the *resolution acuity*. One can measure a variety of other minimum angles including the extent to which a dot of light may be just detectably misaligned from two others, the minimum size of standard test letters which can be clearly read, as in a clinical eye test chart, and so on.

The astronomers' early measurements suggested that the minimum separable threshold was about 1 minute of arc (corresponding to a visual acuity of 1.0 or, in the terminology of the eye clinic, the Snellen[7] fraction of 20/20). We now know that under ideal conditions, most "normal" people can do much better than this. With the ordinary eye chart viewed under optimal conditions, most "normal" eyes will read about 20/10, which corresponds to a visual angle of 30″.

From the analogy of the eye as a camera it has been suggested that one limitation on the visual acuity is the width of foveal cones—because at least one unstimulated foveal cone must lie between adjacent retinal images of two lights in order that the lights be detected as being separate. Since the most recent histological measurements show that the actual size of a foveal cone is such that the angle that a single one subtends at the (exit) pupil is about 24″, it is apparent that this idea explains some of the most obvious aspects of visual acuity. However, it is not necessary to study visual resolution very long before the difficulties with this hypothesis become apparent. The minimum width of a dark line on a white background necessary for visibility (i.e., the minimum visible) is very much a function of the *length* of the line. A long line (a kite string extending high into the air) is much easier to see than a line of similar width but much shorter length.

[5] A minute is a 60th of a degree.
[6] The reciprocal of a number is that number divided into unity.
[7] The numerator of the Snellen fraction represents the testing distance, in this case, 20 feet; the denominator, the distance at which the width of the lines in the smallest identifiable letter subtends 1 minute of arc.

Furthermore, if one measures the aligning power of the eye (i.e., the ability to align two thin lines), one directly over another, an amazing degree of precision is obtained—namely, about 5 seconds of arc. Thus a gap in alignment one-fifth of the diameter of a single foveal cone is readily detectable.

We know next to nothing about how this amazing resolution capacity of the human eye comes about, but we know some of the factors which can influence it. One obvious factor is a defect of the optical characteristics of the eye. Myopia (nearsightedness) or astigmatism (but not hyperopia or farsightedness for a young person with enough accommodation ability to correct the focus) will cause acuity to be poor. These difficulties can usually be overcome with spectacles or contact lenses. Other eye difficulties such as cataracts and retinal diseases are not always as easily/managed, and they also frequently cause deterioration in visual acuity.

Among characteristics of the stimulus, intensity of illumination and the contrast between the test target and the background are important. Other things being equal, the higher the contrast and intensity of illumination, the better the visual acuity. These factors can be studied, using a test target consisting of a series of alternating bright and dark bars called a grating. In any given grating, the width of all dark and light bars will be the same. Different gratings are designed, however, with different width bars, and it is convenient to speak of these differences as differences in spatial frequency as measured by so many black and white cycles per degree of visual angle. These bars can be sometimes square-wave, sometimes sinusoidal, spatial variations in intensity analagous to the time variations in intensity illustrated in Figure 11. Keeping the "average" intensity constant, one can at any given frequency gradually increase the intensity difference (i.e., contrast) between the dark and light bars of the grating until these bars are clearly resolved. The ratio of "modulation" (i.e., contrast) thresholds for sine-wave grating as compared to square-wave grating is about $4/\pi$, which is the ratio of the fundamental components of these two wave forms. The results illustrated in Figure 13A (for sine waves) show many similarities to the flicker results already discussed. Again there seems to be optimal resolution for a grating at an intermediate "frequency" of approximately 5 cycles per degree (i.e., about one dark and light pair every 12 minutes) on the retina. For higher and lower frequencies the performance is clearly poorer. We know as little about the factors which influence the high- and low-frequency acuity curve as is the case in the flicker curve.

Measurements of a similar kind to those illustrated in Figure 13A can also be made on single cells of the cat retina. The data in Figure

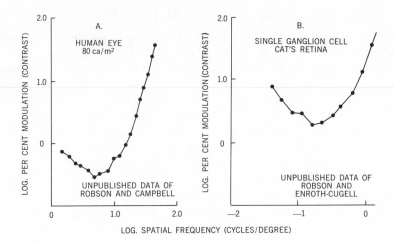

LOG. SPATIAL FREQUENCY (CYCLES/DEGREE)

Figure 13

(A) Threshold contrast (percent modulation) ordinate for sine-wave grating visual-acuity test target as a function of "spatial frequency" (abscissa) scale. Both scales are logarithmic. Background luminance 80 cd/m². Note the similarity to the data in Figure 12. (Unpublished data of J. G. Robson and F. W. Campbell, 1964.)

(B) Similar experiment recorded from a single nerve fiber of the cat's eye. The ordinate represents threshold modulation for change in response of nerve impulse for different spatial frequencies (abscissa). (Unpublished data of J. G. Robson and Christina Enroth-Cugell.)

13B were obtained by placing a microelectrode into a fiber of the optic nerve of the cat and moving a sinusoidal grating past the cat's eye at a very slow rate. The minimum percent modulation at each spatial frequency required to detect a change in the characteristics of the nerve impulses discharging from the cell was recorded. While the resolution of this particular cell of the cat's retina is not nearly as high as that which the human data in Figure 13A illustrate, the similarities in the variation of contrast threshold with width of the bars of the grating (i.e., spatial frequency) in the two cases is evident by comparison of the two graphs in Figure 13.

It has been emphasized that the "graininess of the retina" (as measured by the width of the cones and/or the distance between adjacent cones) is not a satisfactory explanation for all of the facts of visual acuity. It would be wrong to assume, however, that these two things are completely unrelated. One appreciates this by studying the visual acuity for different parts of the visual field. In such experiments it is found that the visual acuity is highest in the very center of the visual field, and it is in the center of the fovea (with which normal eyes do all their critical fine-detail vision) where the density of cones per square millimeter is greatest. As we move out into the peripheral field, the visual acuity falls off very quickly, and so does the density of cones. The distribution of visual acuity in different regions of the retina is illustrated in Figure 14. It is important to note that even within the rod-free center of the fovea, the visual acuity decreases as the peripheral angle increases. While this decrement is probably closely related to the decrease in the density of cones per square millimeter, in the peripheral retina, it should also be pointed out that as one moves from the fovea to the peripheral retina, the number of photo-receptors which converge to each single bipolar cell (and the number of these which converge to each single ganglion cell) also increases rapidly.

MOVING EYES

The data in Figure 14 are worth examination from the viewpoint of the information they supply about our visual environment. If we imagine the eye as a perfectly stationary camera, the data in Figure

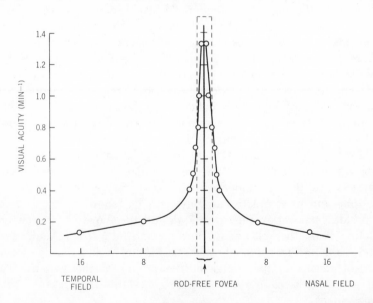

Figure 14

Visual acuity for different positions in the visual field along the horizontal meridian. These are the means of the results from two observers. (From Alpern, 1962.)

14 show that our visual "picture" is very sharp indeed for about one half of one degree in the very center of the visual field, but it becomes less and less clear as we move from the center, and only a very few degrees from the center of the field the "picture" is so completely smudged that virtually no detail is to be seen. Such a system is terribly inefficient. One would not value very highly the services of a photographer who produced pictures like that.

One can make the system remarkably effective, however, merely by attaching to the eyes a series of six extremely fast-acting extraocular muscles which move the eye with incredible speed, more or less around a single center of rotation. Thus the most sensitive region of the fovea may be, in succession, pointed at each object in the visual field, and our visual world appears unified in detail by some very complex temporal integration of the successive impressions of details perceived in this way.

To facilitate this process, a number of different kinds of eye movements have evolved. Some of them are common in even very rudimentary vertebrate eyes, and are reflexly related to the position of the head and the rest of the body. They operate more or less to maintain the status quo. Thus, if a fish is rotated around his body axis, the eyes will rotate in the opposite direction. If his head is depressed the eyes are elevated; if the head is elevated, the eyes are depressed. Comparable movements of our own eyes can be easily shown by stimulation of our semicircular canals or of the macula of the utricle and saccule in the vestibular apparatus of our inner ears. If our bodies are rotated rapidly in a chair, the eyes will undergo the rapid to-and-fro motion called nystagmus. The nystagmus is called jerky because the movement has two components, a slow phase opposite to the direction of rotation of the chair, and a fast phase bringing the eyes back to the front.

Motions of the two eyes in man and primates are almost always synchronized. If you cover one eye and look to your right with the uncovered eye, the eye underneath the cover moves to the right at the same time and in complete harmony with its fellow.

Besides the reflex movements described above, it is convenient to define two other classes of movements—the *versions* and the *vergences*. In a version, the angle that the lines of sight (the line from the object of regard to the center of the pupil) of the two eyes make with each other remains fixed. In a vergence this angle changes during the movement.

There are several kinds of versions and several different kinds of vergences. The convenient distinction of the former are between *saccadic* and *following* movements. Saccadic eye movements are extremely rapid. These are the sudden changes of fixation from one object to another. The velocity of such movement can be as large as 1,000 degrees a second at its peak. During a saccade, that muscle which acts as the agonist contracts, its antagonist relaxes, and the movement is described as *ballistic* or ballistiform.

Following (pursuit) movements are the movements that the eye makes during an attempt to maintain fixation on a moving target. The precision of following movements is extremely good provided the target moves slower than 25 degrees a second. Higher target velocities are not adequately followed by the eyes. The antagonist and agonistic muscles both contract and only a slight excess in tension of the latter suffices to rotate the eye. The stimulus for following motion is provided by the velocity of the movement, presumably by excitation of a suitable velocity detection system. Failure of this line of sight to strike the desired fixation point provides the signal for saccadic movements but not for following movements. The threshold velocity for following movements is only 0.4 degrees a second.

We stated that a vergence movement involves a change in the angle of intersection of the lines of sight of the two eyes. Vergence movements can be classified as horizontal, vertical, or cyclo vergences (i.e., rotations about the lines of sight). Horizontal vergences may be either convergence or divergence. The adequate stimulus for most vergence movement is a disparity in the localization of the visual field in one eye compared to its fellow. This disparity if uncorrected by a fusional vergence movement would leave the observer with a chaotic view of his environment. He would see two visual fields, (one for each eye), and they would be located in different places. Such a condition is called diplopia (double vision). Fusional movements act to reduce the possibilities of diplopia. Obviously, a disparity larger than the amplitude of fusional vergence will still cause a diplopia. The amplitude of fusional vergences can be influenced by certain drugs (alcohol and barbiturates, for example). This explains why one of the classical symptoms of alcoholic inebriation is diplopia. Fusional movements can easily be demonstrated by having an observer fixate binocularly a target relatively close to the nose. Covering one eye will usually cause the lines of sight to diverge under the cover, and upon removal of the cover, the fusional movement will be obvious. The maximum velocity of fusional and other vergence movements is about 20 degrees a second.

A second stimulus to convergence is a change in the stimulus to accommodation (i.e., a stimulus to focus at an object at a different distance). The increased vergence associated with increase in accommodation is called "accommodation vergence." Changes in accommodation, accommodative vergences, and changes in the size of the pupil all occur simultaneously when an accommodation-stimulus change is presented to an observer. Within the physiological range that these quantities vary, each seems to increase as the other increases. A graph describing the relation between the amount of accommodation and the amount of accommodative vergence within this range is invariably a straight line. The slope of such a line varies widely from one individual to the next, but for any given individual, this slope (the rate of change of accommodation with changes in accommodative vergence) is remarkably constant.

The psychophysiological processes which bring about this relation between accommodation, accommodative vergence, and pupil size are still only poorly understood. Nevertheless, it cannot be denied that the neural connection between these three responses plays an important part in the very efficient way that we fixate objects at different distances. If we change our gaze from far to near, the lines of sight of the two eyes converge, the lens of each eye increases its refractive power, and the pupils become smaller, bringing the near object sharply into focus. Thus we can readily look from far to near, without perceiving appreciable blur or diplopia. This is one of the most remarkable achievements of man's truly remarkable visual apparatus.

REFERENCES

The science of color. A report of the Committee on Colorimetry of the Optical Society of America, New York: Thomas Y. Crowell Co., 1953.

Sensory receptors. In *Cold Spring Harbor Symposium on Quantative Biology*, 1965, *30*.

Alpern, M. Muscular mechanisms. In H. Davson (Ed.), *The eye*, Vol. 3. New York and London: Academic Press Inc., 1963, 3–229.

——————, Lee, G. B., and Spivey, B. E. π_1 cone monochromatism. *Arch. Ophthal.*, 1965, *74*, 334–337.

Barlow, H. B., and Sparrock, J. M. B. The role of afterimages in dark adaptation. *Science*, 1964, *144*, 1309–1314.

Blackwell, H. R., and Blackwell, O. M. Rod and cone mechanisms in typical and atypical congenital achromatopsia. *Vision Research*, 1961, *1*, 62–107.

Brindley, G. S. *The physiology of the retina and visual pathway*. London: Edward Arnold Publishers Ltd., 1960.

Dartnall, H. J. A. *The visual pigments*. London: Methuen & Co. Ltd.; New York: John Wiley & Sons, Inc., 1957.

De Lange, H. Research into the dynamic nature of the human fovea-cortex system with intermittent and modulated light. *J. Opt. Soc. Am.*, 1958, *48*, 777–784.

De Valois, R. L. Analysis and coding of color vision in the primate visual system. In *Cold Spring Harbor Symposium on Quantitative Biology*, 1965, *30*, 567–579.

Dowling, J. E., and Wald, G. The role of vitamin A acid. In *Vitamins and hormones*, Vol. 18. New York: Academic Press Inc., 1960, 515–541.

Granit, R. Neural activity in the retina. In *Handbook of physiology*, 1959, 693–712.

Hartline, H. K., and Ratliff, F. Inhibitory interaction of receptor units in the eye of Limulus. *J. gen. Physiol.*, 1957, *40*, 357–376.

Hecht, S. Rods, cones, and the chemical basis of vision. *Physiol. Rev.*, 1937, *17*, 239–290.

——————, Haig, C., and Chase, A. M. Influence of light adaptation on subsequent dark adaptation of the eye. *J. gen. Physiol.*, 1937, *20*, 831–850.

——————, Shlaer, S., and Pirenne, M. Energy, quanta and vision. *J. gen. Physiol.*, 1942, *25*, 819–840.

Le Grand, Y. *Light, colour and vision* (Trans. by R. W. G. Hunt, J. W. T. Walsh, and F. R. W. Hunt). New York: John Wiley & Sons Inc., 1957.

MacNichol, E. F., Jr. Three-pigment color vision. *Sci. Amer.*, Dec. 1964, *211*, 48–56.

Marks, W. B., Dobelle, W. H., and MacNichol, E. F., Jr. Visual pigments of single primate cones. *Science*, 1964, *143*, 1181–1183.

Ogle, K. N. The optical space sense. In H. Davson (Ed.), *The eye*, Vol. 4. New York and London: Academic Press Inc., 1962, 219–423.

Pirenne, M. H., and Marriott, F. H. C. Visual functions in man. In H. Davson (Ed.), *The eye*, Vol. 2. New York and London: Academic Press Inc., 1962, 3–323.

Robson, J. G., and Campbell, F. W. A threshold contrast function for the visual system. *Proceedings of Symposium on the Physiological Basis for Form Discrimination*, Brown University, 1964.

Rushton, W. A. H. The difference spectrum and photosensitivity of rhodopsin in the living human eye. *J. Physiol.*, 1956, *134*, 11–29.

——————. Rhodopsin measurement and dark-adaptation in a subject deficient in cone vision. *J. Physiol.*, 1961, *156*, 193–205.

——————. *Visual pigments in man.* Liverpool University Press, 1962. (The reader will also find a very lucid treatment of this subject in Professor Rushton's 1966 Silliman Lectures soon to be published by Yale University Press.)

——————. Colour blindness and cone pigments. *Amer. J. Optom.*, 1964, *41*, 265–282.

——————, and Westheimer, G. The effect upon the rod threshold of bleaching neighbouring rods. *J. Physiol.*, 1962, *164*, 318–329.

Stiles, W. S. The directional sensitivity of the retina and the spectral sensitivity of the rods and cones. *Proc. Roy. Soc.*, Ser. B., 1939, *127*, 64–105.

_____, and Crawford, B. H.   The luminous efficiency of rays entering the eye pupil at different points. *Proc. Roy. Soc.*, Ser. B., 1933, *112*, 428–450.

Tansley, K.   *Vision in vertebrates*. London: Chapman & Hall Ltd., Science Paperbacks, 1965.

Wald, G.   On the mechanism of the visual threshold and visual adaptation. *Science*, 1954, *119*, 887–892.

_____.   The photoreceptor process in vision. In *Handbook of physiology*, 1959, 671–692.

_____, and Brown, P. K.   Human rhodopsin. *Science*, 1958, *127*, 222–226.

Wright, W. D.   *Researches on normal and defective colour vision*. London: Henry Kimpton, 1946.

_____.   The characteristics of tritanopia. *J. opt. Soc. Am.*, 1952, *42*, 509–521.

HEARING

3

Merle Lawrence

THE COMPLEXITIES OF SOUND

From the moment of your birth every part of your mind and body has been adjusting itself in such a way that the sensations impinging upon your consciousness have been associated with other experiences so as to have meaning. Today when you hear a strange sound that makes you say, "What was that!" it arouses in you some sort of feeling. You may even follow your first exclamation by such a statement as "It sounded like chains rattling." But whether it sounds like anything or not, it undoubtedly arouses in you a feeling of fear, of joy, of bewilderment, of recognition, of curiosity, of alertness, or any of a number of other feelings.

Because sounds play an important role in molding one's everyday behavior, the psychologist is curious to know what the body does with this aspect of environmental energy. But it is difficult to obtain a pure measure of the sensations produced by sounds because they are considerably complicated by what they mean to the individual.

A foreign language is a jumble of noises until, after a little listening combined with some experience, meaning begins to emerge. And yet when these sounds are subjected to physical analysis, they contain, for the most part, the same aspects of energy as your own language. Similarly, music of another country, or the sound of a police whistle, or that of an automobile horn break down into components of vibratory energy. So where does the psychologist start?

There are many approaches. If one were primarily interested in personality or in an individual's adjustment to society, one might accept words and music as they are experienced and study deviations in their meaning, or one might study the process by which meaning is attached to words and other sounds. And there are other methods of study. But to be strictly analytical, one studies the physical nature of sound, finds out what its variables are, and what sensations the simplest of sounds produce. Then, step by step, the process of reception is analyzed. One studies the properties of the peripheral hearing mechanism, then those of the nerve fibers and more central pathways. The more complicated activities of the brain are little understood, and so become an area of study much more advanced than we wish to deal with here.

THE QUALITATIVE COMPOSITION OF SOUNDS

We notice, first of all, that all sounds can be characterized as loud or soft and low- or high-pitched.

Some sounds are so soft that they can just be heard—sometimes, you are not sure whether you heard something or not. If you have never sat in the woods, perhaps behind a blind of spruce boughs, waiting to catch a glimpse of a deer, or a fox, or a rabbit—you have missed a fine experience. As time goes on, you become part of the woods; you hear the wind in the trees way above you, you hear the rustle of leaves, a chickadee, and the far-off low of a cow. These are soft sounds, and you have to listen to hear them. They are carried to you through the medium of air that exists between you and the source and are nothing more, really, than energy conveyed in the form of moving air particles.

If, in this moment of reverie, someone should come up behind you and release a shotgun blast, you would, after you had gotten back into your skin, probably experience a ringing in your ears, and you might say, among other things, that the sound was loud! Here again is energy in the form of moving air particles. In one moment, you have experienced sounds of little and of much energy (referred to as the physical intensity), and you have noted that they are soft and loud.

At the same time you have noted another characteristic of sound, that of pitch: the deep lowing of the cow and the high song of the chickadee. These sounds could be loud or soft depending upon the nearness of the source, but they still maintain their low- and high-pitched quality. Thus the particles of air produce other sensations besides that of loudness.

Were this cow that you heard in the distance to sneak up on you and put her mouth to your ear, her moo might sound as loud as the shotgun blast, but the two sounds would differ in quite another way. The moo of the cow would be gradual in onset whereas the explosion would be sudden. So the sound waves arriving at your ear through the air may exhibit a gradual or a sudden increase in intensity, and somehow this is conveyed to your brain in somewhat its true form, because the former may amaze you but the latter will make you jump sky high.

Suppose now, after these strange experiences in the woods, you were to return home to sit before the crackling wood burning in the fireplace. You might, in listening to the soft music of your record player, notice other characteristics of sound.

A trumpet, a piano, and a violin may all play the same note, and yet you can easily tell which instrument is which. The tones of the instruments must have some characteristic other than that of the single note they are sounding. That which enables you to distinguish among the three is called *timbre,* or it is sometimes referred to as the quality of the sound. Timbre is a most important basic attribute of music and is produced by the impurity of the sound. That is, the note being played is only the fundamental frequency, but each instrument, because of properties resulting from its construction, adds many other high notes varying characteristically in intensity and having a certain mathematical relationship to the fundamental note being played. The presence of these other frequencies gives each instrument its quality, and the ear enables you to tell them apart.

You may also notice, when two or more notes are sounded simultaneously, that the result is pleasing. In this case the resulting sound is called *consonance.* Occasionally, however, two notes produce an unpleasant sound; this is called *dissonance.* The factors that determine the sensation of consonance may be described as those of smoothness or blending. When two notes are sounded simultaneously, they both move the same air particles between the source and your ear. The movement of these particles depends upon the ratio of the two sounding frequencies, and this resultant movement of air particles is picked up by the ear. Thus some ratios produce a smooth, well-blended, pleasing, consonant note, while others produce a rough, harsh, unpleasant, dissonant note.

Another characteristic of the tones that makes them pleasing is that of *vibrato.* If each note were played in a precise and uniform way, somewhat as the beginner does, it would all sound quite mechanical. But by adding a modulation to the frequency and intensity, as well as timbre, the musician gives the tone an artistic, pleasing character. All good singers and most instrumentalists employ the vibrato. Primarily, vibrato is a modulation of frequency in which the listener hears a rapidly varying change in pitch. A special case of vibrato is the modulation of intensity. This is called *tremolo,* an effect most characteristic of organ music, in which the intensity of the note is varied rapidly by a mechanical variation of the air supply to the pipes.

There are many other characteristics of everyday sound that are of considerable interest, but in order to understand them or even to describe them we must have a knowledge of the physical nature of sound. The remarkable thing about all of these phenomena is that the ear can detect and distinguish so many complicated variations in the movement of the air particles.

THE PHYSICAL CHARACTERISTICS OF SOUND

The ancient Greeks, who had proposed that matter is ultimately composed of atoms, had such meager knowledge of the true characteristics of nature that they could make no practical application of their theory. But, in 1808, an English schoolmaster, John Dalton, again proposed an atomic theory. In contrast to the Greeks, however, he used this theory to explain the facts about chemical constituents of matter. Thus, following Dalton's lead, our view today is that gases are made up of atoms combined into molecules. These molecules of air are the particles, the pattern of movement of which is responsible for the propagation of sound. These particles have weight, though they are very minute, and are in constant motion while still maintaining a sort of statistical-mean position. The inherent properties of air can be accounted for in the behavior of the particles, and considering their movement enables us to clarify the concept of transfer of energy from air to ear.

To begin with, imagine a pulsating wall mysteriously suspended in an area of air containing no obstacles. If, connected to this wall, there were an arm operated in such a way that the wall is made to pulsate, the particles immediately around the surface would be compressed together when the wall moves forward and would be pulled apart (causing the air to be rarefied) when the wall moves back. This situation is shown in Figure 1. The compression of the air increases the pressure in this region by crowding the particles of air together. The crowded particles at the outer edge of the compressed area spring farther away, crowding more distant particles.

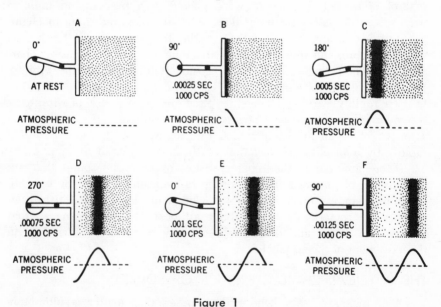

Figure 1

The generation of sound. See text.

Of course, no one particle moves very far itself, but the area of compression continues to move out. In the meantime the wall is moving back and is pulling adjacent particles with it, thus separating them and causing a decrease in pressure below atmospheric; this low-pressure area gradually transcends into the high-pressure area just described. Both of these areas continue to exert their effects on adjacent particles in such a manner that the pressure zones move away from the wall at about 1,100 feet per second.

At the moment the wall has moved back by the amount demanded by the drive arm, the wall starts again to move forward, recompressing the adjacent particles, and the cycle has begun again. The number of times the wall does this each second determines the frequency of the resultant waves; the distance between regions of maximum pressure or maximum rarefaction (minimum pressure) represents one wavelength. These characteristics are all related; the speed of propagation divided by the frequency gives the wavelength. So, for 1,000 cycles-per-second (cps), the wavelength is about 1.1 feet.

Obviously these pressure changes have to occur very rapidly in order to fit 1,000 of them into one second, and the distance any one air particle moves back and forth is not very great. This rapid moving back and forth of the particles caused by the pulsating wall causes the local pressure to fluctuate above and below resting atmospheric pressure, and it is this excess pressure that produces the motion of the *tympanic membrane* in the ear. This is the very thin membrane that closes off the external canal. It connects to the inner ear by three small bones, the *ossicles*.

The difference in pressure above and below resting atmospheric pressure determines the amplitude of movement of the tympanic membrane. Thus, the farther the wall moves in its forward motion, the greater the pressure immediately in front of it is raised; if the tympanic membrane were right next to the pulsating wall, the membrane would move with an amplitude approximately equivalent to the pressure increase. Of course, as these positive and negative pressure regions proceed through the air away from the wall, their energy is dissipated in the form of heat as they force the various particles to move together and apart. This loss of energy causes a gradual decrease in pressure change, an attenuation in the sound, as it proceeds from the source. It is obvious that the amplitude of movement of the tympanic membrane is related to the difference in positive and negative pressure of the air. The characteristic of the sound that gives rise to loudness then can be expressed either in terms of the amplitude of movement of the tympanic membrane or of the pressure difference of the compressed and rarefied regions of air in the sound wave.

The wave characteristics of sound demonstrate another feature quite important for the proper operation of the ear under certain circumstances. Notice that the wheel driving the arm attached to the wall of Figure 1 makes one completed 360-degree rotation for every wavelength of sound generated by the wall. Portions of each wave can be expressed in degrees with respect to any other part of the wave; the maximum pressure point is 180 degrees away from the minimum pressure, and the points of normal pressure are also 180 degrees apart. In this same manner, a wave from one source can be compared with the wave from another source if the comparison is made at the same point or in the same plane in space. Similarly, a wave can be compared with itself at a different point in space, if we keep in mind that the wave is repeated every 360 degrees. When such comparisons are made, the difference in degrees is called the *phase difference*. In dealing with hearing through both ears, which can be represented by two points in space, one must consider the phase or time of sound arrival at each ear. In studying the actions of sound on the ear itself, researchers often must work with the factor of phase relationships in the movement of different parts of various auditory structures.

Pure tones are characterized by a wave pattern like the one shown in Figure 1. As the wall moves back and forth, it generates a variation in air pressure which changes as the sine of the angle at the center of the wheel. Thus a pure tone is called a *sine wave* and the variation in pressure pattern can readily be seen from studying the variations in the right triangle of which the angle at the center of the wheel is a part.

Now it is very seldom that one listens to such pure tones. Probably the only time one is confronted by a pure tone is in a psychophysical experiment or during an audiometric examination of hearing sensitivity. What we hear in everyday life are *complex waves* of various kinds. A complex wave is a sound composed of a number of different pure tones. As this type of sound passes through the air, the positive and negative pressures of the various component frequencies add up algebraically at any one point in space, and so the pressure pattern is not one of a sinusoidally varying pressure but is very complex and, if plotted as we have plotted the sine wave, may appear as a number of unequal hills and valleys above and below resting atmospheric pressure. Figure 2 compares the pressure variations in a pure tone (A) and a complex tone (B). In response to a complex wave, the tympanic membrane moves in and out with several wiggles above atmospheric pressure, then drops to normal and moves with a few wiggles around a negative pressure point. The movement that is set up in the ear follows this pattern.

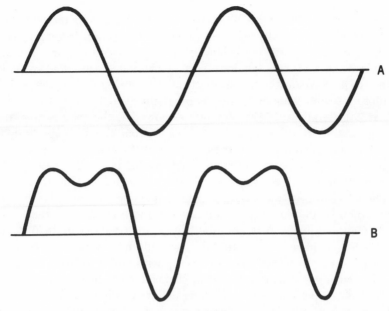

Figure 2

The pressure variation of (A) a pure tone and (B) a complex tone. One wavelength is represented by the distance between points at which the wave repeats itself.

If enough pure frequencies are added together, the resultant sound is a noise. This is called a *white noise* because like white light it is supposed to contain all frequencies. Indeed, if one takes a number of oscillators and makes up a series of pure tones, the result will sound more and more like a noise as more frequencies are added.

Another kind of noise is called *random noise*. Unlike white noise, which is composed of a great many frequencies of sinusoidal shape, random noise contains many frequencies, the amplitudes of which vary randomly with time. In a random noise, a certain frequency may occasionally be reduced to zero; then its amplitude may become great while another frequency is reduced to zero. These fluctuations in amplitude occur in very brief moments of time and are all mixed up in a random manner. Because of these differences, a white noise and a random noise do not sound exactly alike.

THE PERCEPTUAL ASPECTS OF SOUND

PITCH

Frequency is determined by the number of waves passing a particular point during a second. When applied to the ear, frequency means the number of back-and-forth movements of the tympanic membrane in a second. It is hardly ever necessary to determine frequency accurately in auditory problems. However, when necessary, the measurement of frequency can be done with a calibrated cathode-ray oscilloscope, or a wave analyzer, or electronic counters, and in present-day auditory research these instruments are readily available.

It is generally sufficient for us to know that the range of frequencies detectable by the normal human ear is from about 15 cps to 24,000 cps. This range, however, occurs only in very young people, and the upper regions can be measured only by means of special devices. One instrument used a long time ago is the monochord. This is a single-stringed instrument, the string of which is made of a tightly stretched wire which is rubbed with a rosin-covered piece of felt. Another device is the Galton whistle, first described by Francis Galton in 1876. Galton is reported to have carried this device built into a walking cane and to have tested the differences in the upper limit of hearing in people of different ages, and in animals he chanced upon in various zoos.

It is often possible for very young children to hear as high as 24,000 cps, but one of the early aging processes manifests itself in the gradually increasing loss for the high frequencies (presbycusis), so that a person of about the age of 70 may experience a hearing loss at and above 4,000 cps. Thus the mean upper frequency of hearing is around 15,000 cps; so it is commonly accepted that the average range of hearing is from 15 to 15,000 cps.

The lowest frequency of hearing is set at 15 cps, not because this is the lowest frequency that can be heard but because this is the lowest frequency that sounds like a tone. Below this frequency the sound is heard as pulses, and at 1 cps it sounds like a succession of periodic hisses, one occurring each second.

It is possible, when exactly the same frequency is presented to both ears, to hear a different pitch in each—a phenomenon called "diplacusis." This distinction between pitch and frequency should be kept in mind because the sound the listener hears at one stimulating frequency may vary.

We have spoken of the ability to hear frequencies as if the number of cycles per second were the only thing involved in the audibility of tones. However, audibility depends upon a number of factors: the individual, and several other physical characteristics such as wave form, duration, and intensity. The ear is not equally sensitive to all frequencies, so that some require more intensity than others, and we find that as absolute intensity is decreased over the frequency range, the range of frequencies to which the listener is sensitive decreases. We should know something about this relationship.

LOUDNESS

Referring again to Figure 1 (the rotating wheel attached by an arm to a wall), it is obvious that the larger the wheel, the greater distance over which the arm will move. This larger wheel can rotate at the same rate as the smaller wheel so that both create the same frequency. That is, the wall will move back and forth the same number of times in each case so that the same number of regions of compression and rarefaction will pass a particular point in a second. However, the larger wheel, in this period of time, moves the arm farther than does the arm of the smaller wheel, so that the amount of compression and rarefaction is greater, making the pressure above and below atmospheric pressure greater than with the small wheel. When such greater excursions are plotted by means of the sine wave, we find that in both cases the pattern passes through the resting-atmospheric-pressure line at the same point, but that, with the larger-diameter wheel, a much higher point is reached or, in other words, a greater amplitude. When such waves hit the ear, these greater changes cause the tympanic membrane to move farther in and out, and when this amplitude of

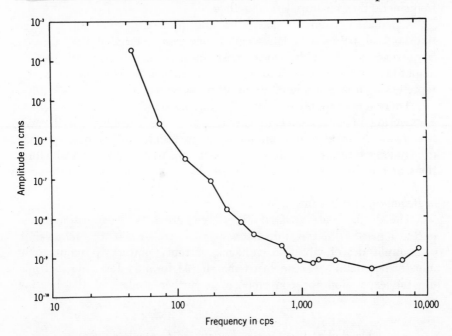

Figure 3

Amplitude of displacement of the tympanic membrane at threshold of hearing for various frequencies. (Data from Wilska; reprinted from E. G. Wever and M. Lawrence, 1954.)

movement is increased, the psychological experience is one of an increase in loudness. Thus, loudness and pitch are both perceptual phenomena, whereas amplitude (or intensity) and frequency are physical phenomena.

By several indirect methods and one direct method, it has been shown that in the frequency region of maximum sensitivity in man, the amplitude of movement of the tympanic membrane is around 10^{-9} cm. The direct measurement was made by Wilska (1935), and is shown in Figure 3. Wilska attached a slender rod to the moving coil of a dynamic loudspeaker and carefully brought the other end of this rod into contact with the tympanic membrane at the attachment of the malleus, the outermost middle-ear bone. A sinusoidal current to the loudspeaker coil drove the tympanic membrane mechanically. With this arrangement, Wilska determined the minimum current necessary for frequencies, from 45 to 9,000 cps, to produce a just audible tone. He calibrated the current-amplitude relationship by means of direct observation of the amplitude of movement with a microscope, but was able to do this only to 270 cps. He determined the amplitudes for the higher frequencies by an extrapolation method.

Calculating from Wilska's data and from data that indicate the threshold of pain for a loud sound, one can determine that for the frequencies to which the ear is most sensitive, it can respond over an amplitude range from 10^{-9} to 10^{-2} cm. This is a very extensive range, representing a magnitude of 10^7 or 10 million units.

There are many other applications in electrical as well as acoustical engineering in which such extensive ranges are encountered. Because it is awkward to use large numbers in expressing, for example, voltage drops along transmission lines or loss of sensitivity to acoustical vibrations in the deafened, the concept of the decibel has been developed (see Lane & Bem, *A Laboratory Manual for the Control and Analysis of Behavior*, in this series).

The decibel (abbreviated dB) is a mathematical expression based on the logarithm of the ratio between two measures of the same kind; e.g., amplitudes of vibration, voltages, currents, powers. Without going into further detail, we can learn the simple formula for a decibel and use the expression for convenience in further studies of the hearing process.

$$\text{Decibel} = 10 \times \log \frac{P_2}{P_1} \text{ , where } P \text{ equals power.}$$

In the study of hearing, however, we are not so much concerned, generally, with *power* as we are in sound pressures or voltages across an earphone. The power of any sound varies as the square of the amplitude, provided the acoustic resistances are the same; so one must keep in mind the units being used to express the characteristics of sound. If one is interested in sound *amplitudes* or pressures, as we have been discussing them, the above ratio has to be squared; in other words, the logarithm has to be multiplied by 2. The formula for a decibel that expresses amplitude ratios then becomes:

$$\text{Decibel} = 2 \times 10 \times \log \frac{A_2}{A_1} \text{ , where } A \text{ equals amplitude.}$$

The most important fact to remember from this discussion is that a decibel is not a unit of sound. It is a *ratio expression,* and so it is possible to express any ratio in terms of a decibel. One could double the light or double the number of people in a room or double the number of leaves on a tree and express the increase in terms of the logarithm of a ratio. The drawback of such a scale is that there never is any real zero value. The zero decibel always refers to some base line. When we expressed the magnitude of an amplitude range as 10^7, our base line was 10^{-9} (see above). If a hearing loss is expressed in decibels, the reference level is the threshold of normal hearing. It happens that at 1,000 cps the accepted level of sensitivity at the threshold of hearing, measured under very accurate conditions, is 0.000204 dyne/cm². But since many different reference levels are used in describing magnitudes of sounds, whenever one is informed that a sound is a certain number of decibels, it is always legitimate to ask what the reference level is. In general, expressions of decibels used in determining levels of sound, such as the noise level in a factory, refer to 0.000204 dyne/cm² as the reference level. Whenever the term *sound-pressure level* (SPL) is seen, it refers to this reference level. Whenever the term *sensation level* (SL) is used, the expression refers to the normal threshold of hearing. Decibels must always have a reference level; if none is given or inferred, then the decibel expression is useless. Many times, however, the reference level is implied or indicated by the above abbreviations.

Before embarking on the explanation of the decibel, we mentioned the fact that the ear is not equally sensitive to all frequencies, some requiring more amplitude than others in order to be heard. It is important to establish this relationship because it expresses the sensitivity of the ear over the audible range of frequencies and tells us just how much of a "hi-fi" device the ear really is. The amplitude level at which a tone is just heard is called the "threshold" of hearing because it represents the crossover point from no hearing to hearing. However, this is never a very clear-cut point because, at this level of sound, a listener is never quite sure whether he hears a tone or not. So the

threshold is taken as the level of intensity at which a listener will say—
50 percent of the time—that he can hear a certain repeated tone. There
is, on the other hand, a move to get away from such a simplified
notion of threshold and to treat the ability to detect a signal in terms
of a statistical decision theory. Such treatment has merit in that it
enables the experimenter to demonstrate small changes in one's ability
to detect signals through the influence of such factors as attention,
expectation, and motivation. These changes are small, however, and
relatively insignificant as far as everyday hearing is concerned.

Ordinarily, in the person with normal hearing, sounds are heard
by both ears as the air around the listener vibrates in response to some
source. It is not sufficient to put a person in a quiet room and reduce
the amplitude of a pure tone until it is just audible. In the first place,
there has to be some means of measuring the sound amplitude at the
position of the person's head; this is complicated by several factors.
The ear is generally more sensitive than most man-made measuring
devices, and the presence of the head and body in the sound field alters
the field differently for different frequencies. The first problem can
be circumvented by measuring the sound at a greater amplitude than
that which can just be heard and then, for testing purposes, by reducing
the amplitude by specific numbers of decibels until the threshold is
reached. Also, although many experiments have shown the effect of
the head and body upon the sound field, this problem can be bypassed—
we can assume that whatever the effect is, it is a constant part of the
listener's hearing process.

For practical purposes, it is sufficient to place a listener in a sound-
isolated room with the listener squarely facing a sound source capable
of emitting pure tones at various controlled intensities. The room must
be one that does not reflect sound waves. Reflected waves might interact with the sound directed at the listener's ears. Such a room is called
"anechoic" because it is free of echos and is made of sound-absorbing
walls. Although there are many different materials that can be used
for making sound-absorbing walls, the most satisfactory is made up of
fiber-glass wedges mounted on the walls with the apex of the wedge
facing the center of the room, as illustrated in Figure 4. Sound hitting
the wedges is mostly absorbed; that which is reflected does so at an
angle into another wedge, where it is absorbed further. The energy of
the sound is turned into minute quantities of heat as the air particles
bounce around within the small spaces of the fiber glass. Use of an
anechoic room allows the ears of the listener to be stimulated by an
almost flat wave front. A sound traveling away from a source spreads
out in a circle from the source. As the distance from the source increases,
the wave front becomes less and less curved with respect to the size

Figure 4

Inside an anechoic chamber.

of the head of a listener. When the wave front is not curved at all, it is called a plane-progressive wave. Since there are no reflections except those from the listener's head and body, there are no complications.

This method of measuring the sensitivity of the ear has been called the free-field method and gives results plotted as curve *a* in Figure 5. Note that the ear is most sensitive between the frequencies of 2,000 cps and 4,000 cps and is least sensitive at the extreme low and high frequencies. It takes about 50 dB more sound to stimulate the ear at threshold for 20 cps than at 2,000 cps, and about 30 dB more sound intensity at 15,000 cps than at 2,000 cps.

This kind of measurement represents a more or less normal listening position, but for strictly quantitative purposes, in determining the sensitivity of the ear, it is important that a single ear be used and that the sound intensity be measured at the entrance to the external canal or just outside the tympanic membrane. This type of measurement can be made by a microphone with a small probe tube attached which can be inserted into the external canal. The threshold curve obtained in this manner is a little different from that obtained by the free-field method and is shown as curve *c* in Figure 5. As would be expected, two ears are more sensitive than one, requiring just about half the sound intensity or 6 dB less of pressure and giving a curve as in *b* of Figure 5.

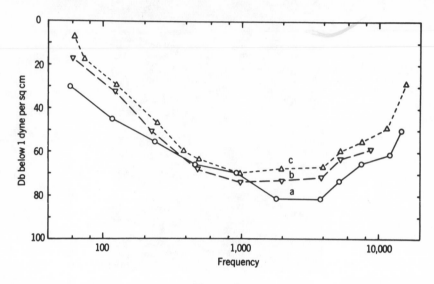

Figure 5

Curves for the threshold of hearing. See text for explanation of curves. (Data from L. J. Sivian and S. D. White. On minimum audible sound fields. J. acoust. Soc. Amer. 1933, 4, 288-324. Reprinted from E. G. Wever and M. Lawrence, 1954.)

At threshold, all frequencies sound equally loud: that is, they are just audible, but, as tones are raised above threshold, equal-amplitude changes at the various audible frequencies do not produce equal loudnesses. Many years ago, two experimenters at the Bell Telephone Laboratories set about to find out how much above the threshold amplitude a tone had to be raised in order for it to sound equally as loud as a 1,000-cps tone when raised to a certain pre-established amount above threshold. Raising the intensity of a 1,000-cps tone 10 dB above threshold gives rise to a certain loudness, whereas a 100-cps tone has to be raised only about 7 dB above threshold to be equally as loud.

Normal conversation is reported to be at a level of about 60 dB above threshold when the speaker is three feet from the listener. A 1,000-cps tone 60 dB above threshold is equally as loud as a 100-cps tone at only 35 dB above threshold. These relationships are shown in Figure 6, taken from the data of Fletcher and Munson (1933), and are known as equal-loudness or *isophonic* contours. This latter term derives from the term "phon," which was invented for the purpose

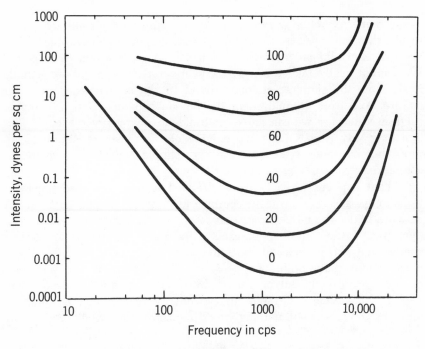

Figure 6

Equal loudness contours from Fletcher and Munson.
(Replotted and printed by permission from E. G.
Wever, 1949.)

of expressing the loudness of a tone as compared to that of 1,000 cps.
Obviously, expressions of physical intensity will not do for expressing
loudness. The phon, therefore, is an expression of the psychological
level of loudness with 1,000 cps as the reference and is equal to the
number of decibels a 1,000-cps tone has to be raised above threshold, or,
other base-intensity level, to sound equally loud to some other frequency. Thus a 100-cps tone 35 dB above threshold is at a 60-phon
level.

INTERACTION OF TONES

Generally, only in experimental situations such as we are describing here does one run into single-frequency pure tones. In everyday
life, sounds are considerably complicated. They occur in what appears
to be a jumble of intensities and frequencies. We may be pleased by
the sounds of our music or our speech, but the music and speech of
one culture may sound discordant and cacophonous to someone from
another. We cannot really say that oriental music is unpleasing, but
we must admit it is different than that of our culture. It is not enough

to say that every child, brought up with the music of his culture, learns to like that kind, just as he learns his native speech. The problem goes deeper: How did an interest in such sounds start in the first place? We cannot really take time to worry about that here; all we can do is see how the simplest of tones sound to the human listener in our culture. And from an analysis of the human capabilities in listening to single frequencies, we can move to studies involving several tones. This is a long way from solving the enigma of the music of different cultures, but one must start from the very simple and then move to the complex. As you can see, we have far to go.

What happens when two pure frequencies are presented together? Commonly, a simple acoustic combination occurs; the particles of air now are under the influence of two sources of compression and rarefaction. But, if the tones are of exactly the same frequency and one is compressing the particles at the same time the other is rarefying them, it is obvious that nothing happens. In other words, if two pure frequencies are exactly out of phase (180° out of phase) a listener will hear nothing. One could put all the energy that could be mustered into these tones and still nothing would be heard: they would completely cancel each other.

On the other hand, suppose these frequencies were in phase, that is, compressing and rarefying together. The pressure increase and decrease would be doubled, though this does not mean that the tone would be twice as loud. As we have noted, loudness is a psychological phenomenon, and as such is dependent upon many other things besides the amplitude of the movement of air particles.

What happens if two tones occurring together are not of the same frequency? Suppose one is 1,000 cps and the other is 1,003 cps. If we were to plot this out, as we have done in Figure 2, it would be obvious that the tones would reinforce and cancel each other three times a second—providing the two were causing the air particles to vibrate at equal amplitude. When you listen to this combination, you hear the 1,000-cps tone waxing and waning three times a second. These are called *beats*, and one tone is said to be beating against the other.

At first, since the frequency difference is minimal, one hears only a slow waxing and waning, a surging of the tone; if the frequency difference is only a fraction of a cycle, it is possible to have these slow beats occurring minutes apart. As the difference increases, the tones begin to have a "roughness," the rate of beating being equal to the frequency difference. This roughness extends up to a difference of around 350 cps. This roughness is the secret of harmony—two people sing notes at nearly the same frequency, but differ enough to give beats to the resulting sound. Try it.

It is also possible to experience beats between frequencies that differ by a few cycles from some multiple relationship, such as 1,000 cps and 2,002 cps. These beats will vary for the same physical reasons as single-frequency beats vary. At certain rates of beats, we find the effect very pleasing, while at other rates, we do not. This is what makes for the consonance and dissonance referred to earlier (page 67).

Beats can also be produced by presenting one low-frequency tone to one ear and another low-frequency tone, differing by a few cps, to the other ear. Such an interesting occurrence gives rise to many questions about the initiation of synchronous neural impulses at the two ears: the neural pathways such impulses travel, the way in which the impulses are combined in some brain center—to name a few.

Two tones of differing frequencies, when separated by a number of cps greater than that which produces beats, give rise to what are called *combination tones.* These are equal to the sum or difference of the two frequencies and consequently are called summation or difference tones. After a little practice one can distinguish these tones.

Ordinarily two tones that are not close enough in frequency to beat can be heard as two separate tones even though the particle motion at the drum membrane is a complex wave form representing one periodic physical sound. Under certain conditions the presence of one tone obscures another, which is then said to be masked—as when an airplane passes overhead and conversation becomes difficult.

In measuring the degree of masking, one has first to set up a careful experiment so as to be able to determine the effect of pure tones on pure tones, noise on pure tones, or any other such combination. Two measures are made: the intensity or loudness level of the tone being masked at the level where it becomes masked (as its intensity is decreased), and the intensity or loudness level of the sound doing the masking. When pure tones have been used to mask pure tones, it has been found that masking is greater for tones close in frequency than for tones widely separated, and that low frequencies are more effective in masking high frequencies than the other way around.

CHANGING TONES

Another interesting aspect of sound perception concerns our ability to discriminate one pitch or one degree of loudness from another. As frequency is raised from low to high, the listener experiences a distinct raising of pitch. If the frequency is increased by discrete steps, there is a distinct pitch heard for each frequency—provided the steps are large enough. This has raised an important question for the psychologist: How many cycles per second must the frequency be changed in order that the listener experience a change in pitch?

There are many ways of varying frequency or intensity to establish the smallest difference in frequency or intensity that can just be noticed. The psychologist must determine the method in accordance with what he wants to find out. Each method chosen gives different results, so the experimenter is confronted with quite a problem.

Since the end of World War II there has been a growing interest in defining human capabilities in such a way that specific data about the limits of human performance would be available to the engineer who designs machines to be operated by men. It was found that information drawn from available psychological literature was inapplicable to practical situations because it generally pertained to maximum human performance under ideal conditions. In order to determine human capabilities for the purposes of an engineering design, the best approach is to duplicate experimentally the less-than-ideal conditions that will limit a man's performance.

Here is an example that shows the importance of human capabilities as a factor in engineering design. In the days when the radio

Table 1

Just noticeable frequency change at various frequencies and levels above threshold (Man).

					FREQUENCY					
		31	62	125	250	500	1,000	2,000	4,000	8,000	11,700
	5	4.0†	6.1	7.6	8.9	8.2	9.4	16	24	50	80
	10	2.7	4.2	5.3	5.3	5.5	6.1	7.2	18	41	68
	15	2.18	3.4	4.1	3.9	4	4.4	5.8	15	36	49
dB LEVEL	20	1.75	3.0	3.7	3.2	3.3	3.9	4.2	12	30	44
	30	1.36	2.9	3.3	2.7	2.7	3.6	3.8	11	29	42
	40	1.26	2.6	3.1	2.6	2.6	3.6	3.8	9.2	23	41
	50		2.2	3.4	2.5	2.1	3.6	3.8	9.2	20	35
	60		2.1	3.4	2.4	1.7	3.4	3.6	8		
	70				2.5	2.1	3.1	3.4			
	80				2.7		3.0	3.6			
	90						2.6				

* The discriminable increment varies considerably with the method used to detect it. The above data were obtained by varying frequency sinusoidally two times per second.
† Just noticeable difference in cycles per second.

range was used almost exclusively as an aid to pilots navigating on instruments, pilots faced a problem of orientation with respect to the radio-range transmitting antennas. In order to determine whether a compass heading was directed toward the range antennas or away from them the pilot had to judge whether the signal was growing stronger or weaker. This situation arose when the pilot did not know where he was with respect to the center of the range. When the pilot was flying toward the station, the signal strength gradually built up, and when he was flying away from the station the signal decreased. In either case, the change was very gradual, but the pilot had to be able to detect a change and then alter his heading if it were necessary. It turns out that, for a small craft flying at 120 miles an hour 5 miles out of station, the rate of intensity change is in the order of 2.6 to 5.5 dB per minute, depending upon the type of terrain over which the pilot is flying. Under these conditions the listening pilot could detect a change of only about 1 to 2 dB per minute. It might have taken him several minutes to determine whether he was approaching or leaving the station. This was not the ideal situation for the detection of change, for laboratory experiments have shown that an observer can best detect small changes in intensity when the changes are fairly rapid.

Because we are interested in the fundamental nature of hearing, we want to know how good an analyzer the ear is—we want to know just how small a change a listener can detect. When we know the capabilities of the ear, we can look for the physical and physiological properties of the auditory system that allow it to perform in this manner.

Many attempts, some as early as 1876, were made to measure a minimal detectable change in frequency (a *difference limen* or DL). The advent of electronic equipment for the generation and control of tones enabled investigators to explore these problems over extensive ranges of frequency and intensity. The most thorough investigation was carried out by Shower and Biddulph (1931) covering a frequency range of 31 to 11,700 cps and an intensity range above threshold of 5 dB to the maximum tolerable level. They used a method whereby a certain standard frequency could be changed gradually to another and back again, in a repetitive manner. By changing the rate at which this variation occurred, they found optimum conditions, which turned out to be a frequency-variation rate of 2 per second.

The results of this experiment are shown in Table 1. The data indicate that the ear can detect a change of as small as 3 cps at 1,000 cps when 80 dB above threshold. There has been some criticism of this technique and so other techniques have been devised, but they all indicate that the ear has considerable resolving power—that is, the ability to detect small changes in frequency. Our important question is, "How does the auditory mechanism accomplish this?"

Table 2

Just noticeable sound-pressure changes at various frequencies and levels above threshold (Man).

FREQUENCY

dB LEVEL	35	70	200	1,000	4,000	7,000	10,000
0		7.9†	6.6	3.7	4.0	5.4	6.4
5	9.3	5.7	4.7	3.0	2.5	4.0	4.7
10	7.2	4.2	3.4	2.4	1.7	2.8	3.3
15	5.6	3.0	2.5	1.8	1.3	2.0	2.4
20	4.3	2.4	1.9	1.5	1.0	1.5	1.7
25	3.4	1.8	1.5	1.2	0.8	1.2	1.3
30	2.7	1.5	1.2	1.0	0.7	0.9	1.1
40	1.8	1.0	0.9	0.7	0.5	0.7	0.9
50		0.8	0.7	0.5	0.4	0.6	0.8
60		0.6	0.5	0.4	0.3	0.5	0.7
70		0.6	0.5	0.3	0.3	0.5	0.6
80			0.4	0.3	0.3	0.5	0.6
90			0.4	0.3	0.2	0.4	
100				0.3	0.2		
110				0.3			

* The discriminable increment varies considerably with the method used to detect it. The above data were obtained by varying intensity at the rate of three cycles per second by beating two tones whose frequency differed by three cycles per second.
† Just noticeable difference in cycles per second.

The same kind of information has been gathered concerning the ability to discriminate intensity changes. Again by electronic means, Riesz combined two tones differing in frequency by a small amount so that their waves interacted, giving a single tone that varied in intensity at a rate equal to the frequency difference of the tones—a phenomenon already described as beating. Should one tone be made less intense than the other, the beating or variation in intensity of the tone will be less marked. By adjusting the frequency and intensity of one of the tones, Reisz (1928) was able to produce a tone that varied in intensity a known amount and at a given rate.

He first determined that the optimum rate of intensity change is about 3 cps. He then explored the DL over a wide range of frequencies and intensities above threshold. These are shown in Table 2. The minimum DL appears to be about 0.2 dB at 4,000 cps when the intensity of the tone is more than 80 dB above the threshold.

THE MECHANICS OF THE EAR

Traditionally, textbooks have divided the ear into four areas: The outer ear, the middle ear, the inner ear, and the nerve pathways. The "outer ear" (Figure 7) consists of the pinna and external meatus. The

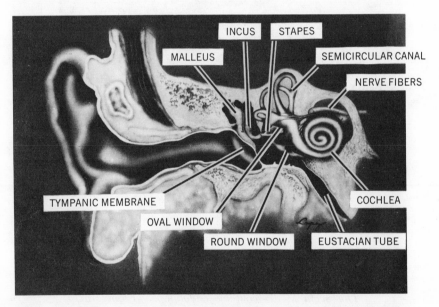

Figure 7

A cut-away of the temporal bone to show the structure of the ear.

tympanic membrane, closing off the medial aspect of the canal, serves as the structure separating this region from the "middle ear." The middle ear is mostly an air-filled cavity connected to the upper throat by a channel (the Eustachian tube). This area also includes another smaller air-filled cavity (the antrum), and many air spaces comprising the mastoid region of the temporal bone. A chain of bones (the ossicles) extends from the membrane to an opening (the oval window) in the petrous region of the temporal bone. Two muscles—the tensor tympani and the stapedius—are attached to this chain (although they are not shown in Figure 7). Posterior to this, there is another opening (the round window) covered by a membrane. Medial to the oval and round windows, within the petrous bone, lies the "inner ear" consisting of fluid spaces, shown in Figure 8, which contain many different

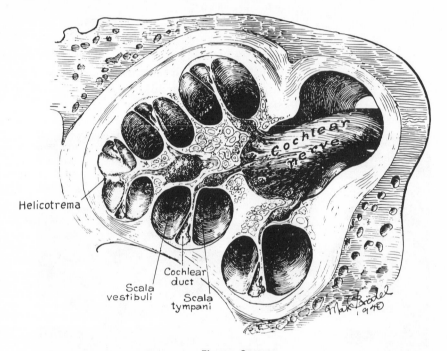

Figure 8

A cut-away view of the cochlea showing the three scalae. The Scala Vestibuli and Scala Tympani both contain perilymph and connect at the Helicotrema. The Scala Media contains endolymph. (From Max Brodel. 1940 Yearbook of the Eye, Ear, Nose, and Throat.)

types of soft tissues as well as openings into the subarachnoid space of the interior skull, and into the endolymphatic duct. Here lie the sensory cells in the organ of Corti described by Corti, in 1851. Structures central to these three are anatomically placed within the central nervous system as the auditory pathways.

These divisions have been so thoroughly taught that there is a persistent tendency to divide the physiological processes of hearing in the same manner. It is common practice, for instance, to use interchangeably the terms ossicular chain, middle ear, and conductive apparatus. Similarly, it is not uncommon to find the terms organ of Corti, inner ear, and sensory apparatus used freely to mean the same thing. Structure and function are related, of course, but classification by structure alone often obscures the workings of the parts.

It is far more meaningful to divide the parts of the ear by function. The first function involved in hearing is the mechanical conduction of vibration, which includes everything from the diffraction of sound by the body and head up to the point where this vibratory form of energy is turned into another form, the nerve impulse. This function

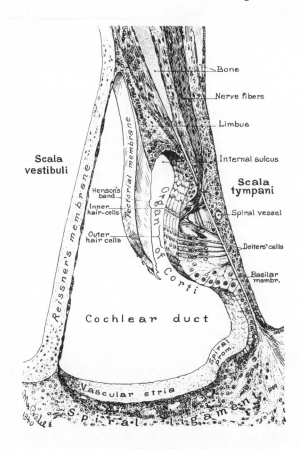

Figure 9

A cross section view of the cochlear duct (Scala Media) to show the organ of Corti. (From Max Brodel. 1940 Yearbook of the Eye, Ear, Nose, and Throat.)

occurs not only in the external ear and middle ear but also in the fluids of the inner ear and in those structural elements responsible for the vibration of the sensory cells.

The second function is the transduction of vibration into an electrical field. This process is an electrochemical activity produced as the result of vibration. (A transducer is a device that converts energy from one form into another—as a light bulb that converts electricity into light; a toaster that converts electricity into heat; a microphone that converts airborne vibration into electricity.)

The electrical field arising from the action of small sensory cells called the hair cells, in the inner ear (Figure 9), stimulates the nerve endings and gives rise to the third process, that of nerve conduction. It is possible to continue this functional analysis by proceeding to the neural process wherein the impulses from the two ears are combined, and finally to the process of cognition and association, but these exciting subjects of future physiological research are too complicated to consider here—even if we knew anything about them.

If these highly specialized cells were like those of other tissues in the body, they could get their energy supply from capillaries, but the nature of their activity precludes the presence of any structure that might dilate, contract, or pulse; the function of hair cells is to be stimulated only by the form of external energy called sound. For this purpose, they are very happily situated. The hair cells are immersed in fluid from which they absorb nourishment without any extraneous, disturbing, influences to make them give off false potentials. They sit between two structures, the basilar membrane and the tectorial membrane, so that if the former is made to move or vibrate, a torsion of the hair cells results. The big drawback lies in getting the energy of airborne sound into the dense fluid that surrounds the hair cells. The vibrational forces of the air cannot penetrate fluids directly without considerable energy loss. As an acoustic medium, air is quite different from a liquid. The tympanic membrane and ossicular chain transfer energy from air to liquid with little loss of energy. A careful study of this achievement fills one with amazement, for here is a mechanical system that accomplishes what audio-engineers have been trying to perfect for many years.

Let us consider the problem of transferring the energy of vibration from the light particles of air to the heavier ones of liquid. To handle such a problem, physicists have formed a concept of the transmittivity of a surface where two mediums meet. This transmittivity is an expression for the ratio of the energy that gets into the fluid to the energy of the airborne sound oscillating at the surface. A very little calculation shows that only 0.1 percent of this energy gets into the fluid, the other 99.9 percent being reflected back. This means that the intensity of sound in the fluid is 30 dB less than that in the air.

The fluid-filled inner ear is encased in hard bone, which necessitates the presence of two openings: one permits vibrations to have access to the fluid, and the other permits vibrations to move the fluids with freedom, unbounded by the bony walls.

Figure 10 shows the exposed inner ear. Sound entering the external

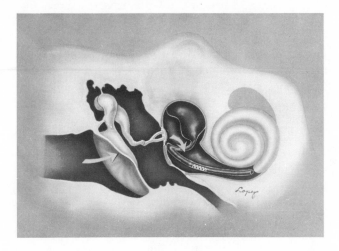

Figure 10

The exposed inner ear showing the ossicular route of entrance for sound vibrations.

meatus hits the tympanic membrane, causing it and its attached ossicular chain to vibrate the inner-ear fluids through the oval window. Aside from conducting the vibrations of the air in the external meatus directly to the oval window, the middle-ear mechanism produces other advantages. Through the structure of its parts it has the characteristic of matching the physical properties of air to those of liquid and so prevents the extensive sound reflection at the interface. There are two mechanisms by means of which the middle ear accomplishes this feat. One involves the difference in area between the tympanic membrane and the footplate of the stapes; the other is a lever action brought about by the positional relationship of the three ossicular bones.

Measurements which have been made in man show the tympanic membrane to have, on the average, an area 21 times greater than that of the stapes footplate. Because the membrane is not like a piston but is like the cone of a loudspeaker—fastened down around its edge— its effective area of movement is somewhat less than its total area.

Experimental measurements have shown this effective area to be about two-thirds that of the total area, or 14 times that of the stapes. This means that the pressure per unit area on the drum membrane must be transferred to the smaller area of the footplate. Such a situation decreases the air-liquid interface disadvantage by 23 dB, thus increasing the effectiveness of the oval-window vibrations by this amount.

Some additional advantage is gained through the lever action of the ossicles. Experimental measures of this have not been too accurate, but what there are indicate a gain in pressure of about 1.31 to 1, which again decreases the air-liquid interface disadvantage, although only by about an additional 2.5 dB.

In the bird, a creature that hears very well, this peculiar relationship of three bones is missing. Instead, there is a straight connection, called a *columella*, between the tympanic membrane and the footplate. Thus the bird's ear relies entirely on areal ratio to transfer vibrations from air to liquid.

In the human ear, the combination of the areal ratio and lever action gives a total increase in effectiveness of vibration transfer of 25.5 dB, which fails by 4.5 dB in making up for the loss of energy at the air-liquid interface. This indicates that the middle-ear mechanism is not perfect. The data upon which these figures are based may be somewhat in error because of difficulties in making the experimental determinations. On the other hand, if the figures are correct, removal of the middle-ear system should result in a hearing loss of only 25.5 dB, and not the theoretical 30 dB. This is providing the round window, which normally allows for freedom of movement of inner ear fluids, is protected from vibrations. In the absence of a normal middle ear sound can strike both windows simultaneously and nullify fluid movement.

We have described the final act in the vibratory process as stimulation of the hair cells. It was once thought that the nerve fibers were stimulated directly by mechanical vibration. In 1683, DuVerney, who did not know there was fluid in the inner ear, guessed that the nerve fibers were spread out on one side of the spiral osseous lamina, the spiral of bone that supports one end of the basilar membrane, and that stimulation was brought about through the resonant vibration of parts of this bony structure in response to aerial vibration transmitted to the ear.

Any object will vibrate sympathetically (resonate) to vibrations in the surrounding medium—whether air or liquid—when it inherently has the same natural frequency as the vibrations. Certain strings in a piano will resonate to frequencies to which they are tuned. This is the effect by which certain singers are reported to be able to break a glass by singing specific notes; they sing a note at the resonant frequency of the glass—which causes the glass to vibrate sympathetically and shake itself apart.

According to DuVerney's theory, this bony shelf—the spiral osseous lamina—not only responds to vibrations but is capable of responding differently to different frequencies. Because the lamina is broader at the base than at the apex of the cochlea, the lower frequencies cause the basal end to vibrate while the higher frequencies produce vibrations near the apex. The nerve fibers spread out over this partition are thus stimulated selectively by different frequencies and serve to analyze the sound. This is actually the reverse of what we know today. It is the basilar membrane that vibrates, and, where the lamina is broad, the membrane is narrow, which reverses the areas of vibration for different frequencies.

About 200 years later, Helmholtz (1870) proposed a theory also incorporating the resonance principle. Helmholtz designated specific resonators that supposedly enable specific nerves to carry messages to the brain. We know now that Helmhotz's theory is untenable for at least two very important reasons. Further careful anatomical observations have failed to indicate the presence of structures capable of resonating in any isolated manner, and such characteristics of specific resonance are not mechanically compatible with certain psychophysical observations. Any device sharply tuned, when caused to vibrate, will do so for a relatively long period of time. This would indicate that once a tone had been sounded and the resonator activated, the sensation of tone would persist for some time after cessation of the stimulus. But we do not find this phenomenon in the ear. In order for a resonator rapidly to cease its activity after it is no longer driven, the resonator must be highly "damped" so that vibrations are killed off rapidly. (A tuning fork can be damped by putting it in a vat of oil.) But a highly damped resonator responds to a broad band of frequencies and thus loses its sharp response to a particular frequency.

In 1886, Rutherford presented a lecture, "On the Sense of Hearing," before the members of the British Association for the Advancement of Science. In his lecture, he described a theory of nerve pulses per cycle within the inner ear; his theory was based on principles similar to those which cause vibration to be produced when a sound wave falls on the metal diaphragm of a telephone. Rutherford believed that there is no analysis of complex vibrations in the cochlea, but that all vibrations, no matter of what frequency or amplitude, or how complex, are directly portrayed by nerve impulses to the brain. The entire stretch of the basilar membrane and all of the hair cells are supposed to be involved for every tone. Although he was aware of experiments that had demonstrated a frequency of no more than 1,400-cps as possible in a nerve fiber, he chose to ignore these as not being accurate and expressed the notion that frequencies of more than 10 times this value were probably possible.

There is evidence against this theory. If any error were made in the experiments that had been carried out on nerve-recovery rates after firing, it was probably in overestimating the repetitive firing rate of nerve fibers. A maximum frequency for the best single fibers is accepted as 1,000-per second, and the auditory nerve fibers do not appear to be any different from other nerve fibers in this respect. There is the possibility that the single fibers may not fire every time in response to each wave of a stimulating sound but may drop out while others fire. Thus when the bundle of nerve fibers are taken all together, the total rate may correspond to the frequency of the sound. Wever and Bray (1937) proposed this as the "volley theory," but not strictly in defense of Rutherford's notion of basilar-membrane action.

Rejecting Helmholtz's notion of specific resonators, and modifications of his theory, Ewald, in 1898, proposed a "standing-wave" pattern for the basilar membrane as it responds to sound vibrations. Apparently he thought of waves as starting at the basal end of the basilar membrane, traveling to the apex with little attenuation, and reflecting back toward the base. This would establish a series of loops and nodes between the two ends. The loops and nodes would vary in number and width for different frequencies. As the frequency rises, a greater number of loops, each covering a narrower region, would be produced.

At the turn of the century, another class of theories arose which purported to establish some form of peripheral analysis of sounds without resonance or standing waves. These are the so-called "traveling-wave" theories; they are based upon the concept of a displacement wave progressing along the basilar membrane. There have been many of these theories but they all start with the observations of Békésy, reported in 1928. His work on this subject has been so thorough, accurate, and illuminating that, among many other awards, he won the 1961 Nobel Prize in Medicine and Physiology.

In 1928, Békésy called attention to the fact that the essential difference among the proposed theories lay in their divergent assumptions concerning the magnitude of the elasticity and friction characteristics of the basilar membrane. At first, because direct observation of the movement of the basilar membrane is quite difficult, Békésy designed a model of the ear in order to reproduce the actual conditions as accurately as possible and thus, by observation, a choice among the different theories became possible.

After carefully determining the viscosity of the perilymph, the size of the helicotrema where the scala vestibuli joins the scala tympani (shown in Figure 8), and the varying width of the basilar membrane, Békésy built a model (Figure 11). First, he fashioned a rec-

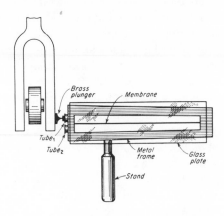

Figure 11

Békésy's model of the cochlea. (From Békésy, 1928).

tangular frame, rather long and narrow, along the middle of which ran a thin metal band so that the cavity of the frame was divided into two

Figure 12

The "basilar membrane" of the model shown in Figure 11. (From Békésy, 1928.)

long narrow channels. The middle of the metal band shown in Figure 12, had a long tapering slot shaped as the basilar membrane would be if stretched to full length, narrow at the base and wide at the apex. Just beyond the wide end of this slot was a hole to represent the helicotrema. The slot was covered by a membrane made from the kind of rubber solution used by bicyclists to patch tires. Faced with the problem of determining the proper thickness of this membrane to make it correspond with the elastic properties of the basilar membrane, Békésy referred to an earlier experiment by Wittmaack. In 1917, Wittmaack had made the observation, in histological sections of guinea pig ears, that intense pure-tone stimulation produced an injury to the sensory cells at a place along the basilar membrane corresponding to the frequency of stimulation. This injury was near the base for high tones and near the apex for low tones. In order to reproduce this effect, Békésy increased the thickness of his rubber membrane as the wide end of the slot was approached. The thickness of the membrane was varied until loud tones introduced into the model produced holes in the membrane in the same location as the site of injury in Wittmaack's guinea pigs.

The frame, containing this metal insert with a rubber membrane, was mounted on one of its long sides in a holder; two glass plates were cemented to the open sides so as to form an upper and lower trough above and below the rubber-membrane-covered dividing plate. The troughs were filled with either a dilute solution of glycerine in water or just plain water, depending upon the size of the model, to simulate the fluids of the inner ear.

At the end of each trough was a rubber-covered opening representing the oval and round windows. Into the "oval window" a brass plunger, attached to the tine of a tuning fork, was inserted. Carbon particles were put into the fluid of the upper trough so as to cover the rubber "basilar membrane" evenly.

When the tuning fork was made to vibrate, the carbon particles were all forced toward the "helicotrema," indicating the presence of a traveling wave going in the direction of the helicotrema. When a steady state of vibration was reached, the pressure variations above the membrane equalized so that there was no longer a movement of the carbon particles over the helicotrema.

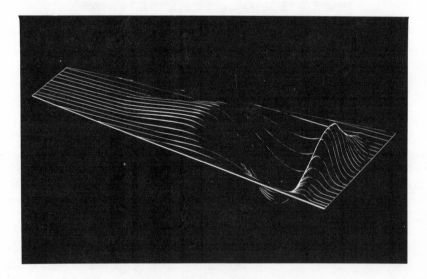

Figure 13

The traveling wave.

Depending upon the frequency, the portion of membrane extending from the stapes to a certain point along the membrane all moved up and down in phase, increasing in amplitude up to this certain point. Beyond this point, toward the helicotrema, there was a sudden reversal in phase, followed by a series of small waves becoming progressively smaller in wavelength and amplitude. These observations of the traveling wave were later confirmed by experiments on cadaver cochleas. The form of the traveling wave is illustrated in Figure 13.

From the time of that initial observation, to the present date, Békésy has determined in a very precise way many of the actual physical characteristics of the inner ear. The traveling wave and the measurements have been used by many others who have proposed mathematical expressions for basilar membrane motion in response to sound, but occasionally the traveling-wave theory itself has been subject to criticism. So, in 1956, Békésy reviewed the theories and showed that by manipulating only two independent physical variables—the absolute stiffness and the coupling of adjacent parts—he could produce a continuous series of vibratory patterns merging each of the four major theories presented here. Such considerations move directly toward answering the questions: What precisely is the pattern of vibration on the basilar membrane, and how are the transducers activated in response to vibrations introduced into the fluids of the inner ear?

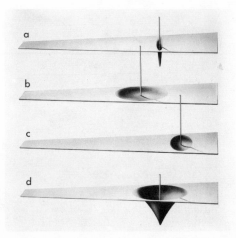

Figure 14

The depression caused by a point force on membranes differing in absolute stiffness and coupling of adjacent parts. (a) Resonance (b) Frequency (c) Traveling Wave (d) Standing Wave.

Again Békésy resorted to membrane models, but, in this case, the elastic property of the membrane was varied. Békésy had shown earlier that the stiffness of the basilar membrane varies, being about 100 times stiffer near the base than at the apex. This slope of stiffness, therefore, was kept constant, but absolute stiffness and inherent coupling between adjacent parts of the membrane were varied. The displacement resulting from a point force and the pattern of vibration produced by a continuous tone on different kinds of fluid-immersed membranes are shown in Figure 14.

If the membrane were made up of a series of thin elastic fibers stretched across the model frame there would obviously be no coupling between them, and a point force, such as a needle, would make a sharp localized depression in one fiber only (Figure 14). This condition is in accord with the Helmholtz resonance theory of freely vibrating resonators; a limited lateral spread of deformation results. If this membrane is immersed in fluid and a steady sinusoidal vibration introduced, the pattern shown in Figure 15a is produced.

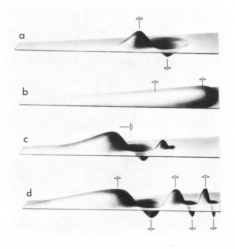

Figure 15

Motion of the model "basilar membrane" produced by a sinusoidal stimulus. (a) Resonance (b) Frequency (c) Traveling Wave (d) Standing Wave.

If the same 100-to-1 slope of stiffness over the length of membrane is maintained, but the basic over-all stiffness is increased by coupling the elastic fibers together with a plastic sheet, a point force applied to the membrane will produce an elongated flat deformation, as shown in Figure 14b. When immersed in fluid and subjected to vibration, the entire membrane moves up and down following exactly the movements of the driving "stapes," in accordance with Rutherford's telephone theory, as shown in Figure 15b.

By decreasing the thickness of the elastic sheet that couples the transverse fibers together, the basilar-membrane action promulgated by the other two classes of theories could also be duplicated. As the thickness decreases, the deformation produced by a point force increases, as shown in Figure 14c. A steady tone presented at the "stapes" of the model under these conditions produces a traveling wave just as was seen in the cadaver specimens and illustrated in Figure 15c.

With continued thinning of the membrane, the same point force sharply displaces the membrane still further, Figure 14d. The traveling waves produced by the same steady tone now become shorter and travel farther so that they are reflected from the far end of the membrane and produce standing waves as Ewald had described (Figure 15d).

We have pointed out that the pattern of vibration is determined by two variables: the absolute stiffness of the membrane and the coupling between its adjacent parts. Thus it is possible to go continuously from one pattern to another, so that an infinite number of intermediate patterns can be produced. What about the myriad of other theories one reads about? Békésy says, "Additional vibratory patterns have been proposed, some of which the writer has tried to verify on models, but the conclusion has been reached that they are only drawings and have no physical existence."

The question of which pattern of vibration is the actual one boils down to the more readily studied question of what are the actual values of the stiffness and coupling along the basilar membrane. On this basis, the traveling-wave theory wins out.

In the first place, Békésy reports seeing the traveling wave pattern along the basilar membrane in various mammals. Also, in experiments in which the tip of a needle was pressed perpendicularly on the surface of the basilar membrane of several vertebrates (guinea pig, mouse, cat, pigeon, cow, elephant, and human), the resulting deformation was always of the type shown in Figure 14c, almost circular. This indicates that the coupling between adjacent parts of the basilar membrane is too great to permit a resonant type of action. A side view of the deformation shows that the stiffness of the basilar membrane is too great to permit standing waves.

Discovery of this rather broad pattern of action on the basilar membrane complicates things considerably, however, because it still does not tell how subjects can discriminate pitches only 3 cps apart. This brings us to the frontiers of research on this problem, for, at present, there are only theories about how this fine analysis takes place—current theories are based on the relationship between the hair cells and the intricate pattern of neural innervation by the auditory nerve.

A description was given earlier of the process of transduction whereby the vibrations, entering the fluids of the inner ear, are transformed into an electrical field which stimulates the nerve endings, giving rise to the nerve impulse. Thus, two basic types of potentials are recorded from the ear: those arising from the sensory cells and those arising from the nerve fibers. The response from the hair cells was first described by Wever and Bray in 1930 and consequently has been called the Wever-Bray effect. Generally, an electrode of platinum foil is placed on the round-window membrane. This electrode is connected through a high-gain amplifier to any desired measuring device: a voltmeter, a cathode-ray oscilloscope, a loudspeaker.

A remarkable characteristic of these sensory-cell potentials is that they follow electrically the form of the acoustic wave presented to the ear whether the sound is a complex wave, or a noise, or a pure tone, or a beating tone. This is quite unlike the nerve impulse that follows; the nerve impulse is a spike of electrical change that does not vary in its magnitude regardless of the intensity of the sound stimulus. All of the different types of vibrations that are presented to the ear are first reproduced more or less faithfully in the cochlear potential of the hair cells and then coded somehow into the spike potentials of the nerve fibers. Precisely how this is done or how the many complicated wave forms of sound can be carried by these simple neural responses is not known. You will find more extensive discussions of these problems in Charles Butter, *Neuropsychology*, in this series.

The cell bodies for the most peripheral neurons lie in a channel, Rosenthal's canal, that spirals around the center of the cochlea, giving off fibers to the hair cells all along the way. These fibers follow paths in the form of bundles that pass for as much as half a turn of the cochlea, sending out many fibrils to many hair cells, so that any one fiber may innervate innumerable hair cells, and any particular hair cell may be contacted by several different fibers. It is known that the single fibers that pass centrally from these cell bodies into the brain stem are much more specific for frequencies than the general pattern of basilar membrane activity would suggest, so some sort of interplay between traveling wave and nerve fiber must take place. Békésy has called this characteristic "funneling," because the broad response of the basilar membrane seems to be narrowed down. We know nothing at the present time about how this takes place, but the effect does seem to be the first step in the physiological analysis of different frequencies. The specificity of fibers seems to get sharper as one proceeds up the neural pathways to the brain. The necessity for precision in the nerve potentials can be illustrated by considering the phenomena attributed to listening with both ears.

THE ADVANTAGE OF TWO EARS

A person with one functioning ear can get along quite well in this world as long as he is required only to detect and discriminate sounds. However, as soon as he is required to localize a sound, or rotate his attention from one sound source to another, he is at a disadvantage without two equally sensitive ears.

The ability to localize a sound source has been the subject of much investigation for a number of years, and results have indicated that for actual sound sources, it is possible for an observer to localize various frequencies with an error of less than 10 degrees for all frequencies except those in a very small range centering around 1500 cps. From these studies it has been revealed that one of two basic mechanisms, depending upon the frequency, is involved in this localization.

Those frequencies of a long wavelength, relative to the distance between the two ears, encounter very little interference from the head. The intensity of the tone is approximately the same, therefore, at the two ears. However, any particular wave of compression will reach the near ear a fraction of a second before reaching the other. At standard conditions, the velocity of sound in air is 3.44×10^4 cm/sec and the average distance between tympanic membranes on a human head can be taken as 9 cm (3.6 in.). Therefore, it takes a compression wave 0.029 milli-seconds to travel one cm or 0.26 milli-seconds to travel from the position of one tympanic membrane to the other if we consider the sound source as a wave approaching the head from the side.

If the head is rotated with respect to the plane of the approaching sound wave the time difference of arrival of the compression wave becomes less. Similarly, as the frequency is raised for any head position, the absolute time difference remains the same, but because of the shortening wavelength, the difference in time of arrival between compression waves decreases. At the frequency where the distance between tympanic membranes exceeds one-half of a wavelength, the compression wave in the far ear seems to precede that in the near ear because compression wave A reaches the far ear just before compression wave B reaches the near ear, B reaches the far ear just before C reaches the near ear, and so on. (As described earlier, the pressure amplitude of the compression-rarefaction wave is mathematically represented by the length of a line dropped from the rotating radius and perpendicular to a horizontal diameter of the circle. Thus a wave whose region of compression reaches the far ear just as the region of rarefaction reaches the near ear would produce movements at the two tympanic membranes 180° out of phase.)

As frequency is increased, the wavelength decreases which gives rise to another effect: the head has a greater influence upon the passage of the sound waves through the air and because of this shadowing effect the intensity at the far ear becomes less, relative to that of the near ear.

It is easy to see, then, that there are two fundamental mechanisms behind the ability of an individual to localize sounds: one, based on phase difference, and another, on intensity differences. Recent experiments have determined how fine these differences can be and still be appreciated by the human ear in localizing sound.

The data that most nearly furnish the information desired for this presentation come from research reported by A. W. Mills (1958). For a sound source located directly in front of the observer, the minimum detectable change in direction—as the source was moved from the straight-ahead position—occurred for the frequencies between 250 and 1,000 cps, and was found to be about 1 degree. As the frequency was increased from 1,000 to 1,500 cps the detectable angular change approached a maximum. The frequency at which this maximum occurred varied with the position from which the change was made, but at all positions, the minimal detectable change in direction dropped to another minimum between 3,000 and 6,000 cps and approached another maximum around 8,000 cps.

This series of experiments, as well as earlier ones, demonstrates that the ability of a listener to detect changes in position at frequencies below 1,400 cps depends primarily upon temporal cues, or more specifically, for steady pure tones, upon the difference in time of arrival of the compression segment of the wave as it activates the two ears. The smallest average value of the minimum detectable phase change was found to be 1.4 degrees at a frequency of 250-cps when the variation in phase was made from a zero phase difference at the two ears.

Intensity differences seem to provide the basis for azimuth discrimination for high frequencies—frequencies which have a wavelength shorter than the distance between the two ears.

In the experiments of Mills, the threshold for an interaural difference in intensity was found to be about 0.5 dB.

It would appear from these experiments that the ability of humans to localize sounds is quite refined. However, we have considered only pure tones which are seldom encountered in everyday life; more practically, one should consider the ability to localize noises or music or the spoken voice, but for our purposes here, the ability to localize a pure tone is adequate.

REFERENCES

Békésy, G. v. Zur theorie des Hörens; Die Schwingungsform der Basilarmembran. *Physik. Zeits,* 1928, *29,* 793–810.

Corti, Alphonse. Recherches sur l'organe de l'ouie des mammifères. *Zeits, f. wis Zool.,* 1851, *3,* 109–169.

DuVerney, Joseph Guichard. *Traité de l'organe de l'ouie.* Paris, 1683.

Ewald, J. R. Ueber eine neue Hörtheorie. *Wien. Klin, Wochenschr.,* 1898, *11,* 721.

Fletcher, H., and Munson, W.A. Loudness, its definition, measurement, and calculation, *J. acoust. Soc. Amer.* 1933, 5, 82-108.

Helmholtz, Hermann L. F. *Die Lehre von den Tonempfindungen als physiologische Grundlage für die Theorie der Musik,* 3rd ed. 1870. Eng. trans. by Ellis, A. J. *On the sensations of tone,* 2nd Eng. ed., 1885.

Mills, A. W. On the minimum audible angle. *J. acoust. Soc. Amer.* 1958, *30,* 237–246.

Riesz, R. R. Differential intensity sensitivity of the ear for pure tones. *Phys. Rev.,* 1928, *31,* 867–875.

Shower, E. G., and Biddulph, R. Differential pitch sensitivity of the ear. *J. acoust. Soc. Amer.* 1931, *3,* 275–287.

Wever, E. G. Theory of hearing. New York: John Wiley, 1949.

Wever, E. G., and Bray, C. W. Action currents in the auditory nerve in response to acoustical stimulation. *Proc. nat. Acad. Sci., Washington,* 1930, *16,* 344–350.

_____. The perception of low tones and the resonance-volley theory. *J. Psychol.,* 1937, *3,* 101–114.

_____. Auditory nerve impulses. *Science,* 1930, *71,* 215.

Wever, E. G., and Lawrence, M. Physiological Acoustics. Princeton University Press, 1954.

Wilska, A. Eine Methode zur Bestimmung der Hörschwellenamplituden des Trommelfells bei verschiedenen Freguenzen. *Skand. Arch. Physiol.,* 1935, *72,* 161–165.

CHEMICAL SENSITIVITY

David Wolsk

4

Stories of male gypsy moths detecting the odor of a female moth from seven miles away and the exceptional sensitivities of professional food and wine tasters are typical of the legendary side of taste and smell. They add considerably to the mysteries of chemical sensitivity, mysteries that persist despite a considerable amount of excellent research.

In addition to smell and taste, the concept of chemical sensitivity encompasses general reactions to chemicals—such as occur on the surface of the skin. There is also evidence that the functioning of internal organs involves chemically sensitive receptors. However, we shall confine this chapter to taste and smell—the two chemical processes that have been most widely investigated.

Although most psychology books spend little time on these sensory systems, some events of history may highlight their importance in human behavior. The early voyages of discovery—Marco Polo's overland journey to China, Christopher Columbus' transatlantic sail, and Vasco da Gama's voyage around the tip of Africa—were all largely motivated by a great demand in Europe for the spices of the East. The forces of colonialism started with a hunger for better-preserved and tastier food. Today, the continuing influence of taste and smell is underscored by research projects designed to find ways to train American diplomats and military representatives to eat and at least look as though they are enjoying such regional ceremonial delicacies as sheep's eyes.

A recent and dramatic demonstration of the importance of chemical sensitivity concerns what may be termed olfactory abortion. When impregnated female rats are housed in a cage with unfamiliar male rats, there is a significant decrease in the number of successful births. That this is a consequence of the odor of the unfamiliar males was shown in control experiments using females whose olfactory epithelium had been removed. The presence of the strange males had no similar effect on these anosmic (no smell) females (Parkes and Bruce 1961).

This touching finding of an "olfactory morality" among our rodent forebears may lead one to wonder, aside from the advertising promises, about the actual powers of perfume and other odors. To speculate about similar functions for taste, perhaps kissing is our civilized way of picking a mate by taste.

Although the unsolved mysteries of chemical sensitivity encourage this kind of speculation, there is a large and rapidly growing body of excellent anatomical, electrophysiological, and behavioral data more deserving of attention. As we discuss these data and the theories they have engendered, taste and smell shall be considered separately (although they are, of course, closely related).

SMELL

Two necessary characteristics of odorous substances are volatility and solubility: after the molecules of these substances have diffused into the atmosphere and then been drawn into the nasal passages, they must be soluble in water or fat to become effective olfactory stimuli. The olfactory receptor cells are contained in the olfactory epithelium; in man the olfactory epithelium lies in the upper back part of the nasal cavity. The total area of the epithelium is about the size of a dime (2.5 sq. cm.); because of its position, above the main air stream during normal respiration, one gets advantages from sniffing as this sets up eddy currents of air toward the epithelium.

An olfactory stimulus must penetrate the liquid covering of the olfactory cells. This covering consists of secretions from many serous and mucous glands located near the epithelium. After being dissolved in these bathing fluids, an odorant must be adsorbed by the olfactory epithelium, thereby finally making contact with the receptor cells. What this "contact" consists of is presently unknown.

One of the chemical properties that seems important in the contact is the molecular weight of the substance—possibly because adsorptive power tends to decrease with increasing molecular weight. To be exact, the molecular weight must be between 17 and 300. Within any similar series of organic substances, there is generally an optimal molecular weight, above and below which the substances are less odorous.

Of all the chemical elements, only seven are odorous: flourine, chlorine, bromine, iodine, oxygen (as ozone), phosphorus, and arsenic. Six of these are at the bottom of the electrochemical series, suggesting another possible structural relationship. Much attention has also been paid to the nature of the bonds between the atoms of odorous molecules. If the molecules are not saturated, it is possible for a chemical attachment, or bond, to be made with the receptor cell. Also in organic compounds, the placement of the "exchangeable groups" seems related to both the strength and the quality of the compound as an odorant.

These chemical properties of odorants are mentioned not to make the reader run to a chemistry textbook but, rather, to indicate why much research and theorizing in olfaction takes the form it does. The existence of relationships between chemical properties and odor, such as those mentioned (and many more), encourages the researcher interested in understanding what makes an odorous substance have its own individual odor. Unfortunately, efforts to understand this relationship continue to be frustrated by inconsistencies and incompatibilities.

Much of this search depends upon more detailed and precise information concerning the receptor cells. Any theory about the stimulation process has to be consistent with the structure of the receptor as well as the chemical structure of odorants. Figure 1, which is a drawing reconstructed by De Lorenzo (1963) from thousands of pictures taken

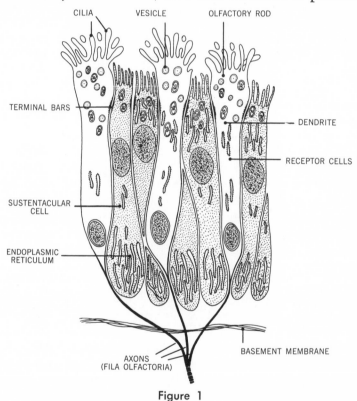

Figure 1

Drawing (constructed) to show the cellular structure of the olfactory epithelium.

through an electron microscope, illustrates the most recent level of description of the cellular structure in the olfactory epithelium. The exposed surface of the oval-shaped receptor cells contains up to 1,000 cilia, or finger-like processes, variously described as being 1 to 100 mμ in length. They increase tremendously the surface area of each cell. Based on an estimate of the dimensions of the cilia, a calculation of 600

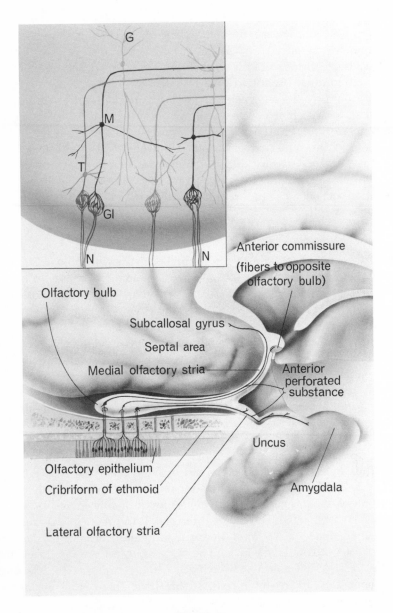

Figure 2

Diagram of neural arrangements coming from the olfactory epithelium. The inset shows olfactory nerve filaments (N) entering the olfactory bulb from the olfactory epithelium. Tracing upward from a filament, one finds a glomerulus (Gl), a tufted cell (T), a mitral cell (M), and a granular cell (G).

cm² has been reported as the total surface area of the receptor cells. This is quite an increase over the 2.5-cm² surface of the olfactory epithelium.

This large surface area is probably one of the factors responsible for the extraordinary sensitivity of the olfactory system. Another factor may be the neural arrangements (see Figure 2) coming from the receptor. Each receptor cell tapers down to an extremely small unmyelinated nerve fiber (0.2 mμ diameter) which passes through the cribriform plate of the skull and then enters the right or left olfactory bulb. Thus, the olfactory sensory cells in humans are like the primary sensory cells of insects, combining both receptor and conduction functions. This elimination of one synapse results in an extreme sensitivity for the single sensory cell.

Another mechanism that increases sensitivity occurs at the first synapse of the neural pathway. In the olfactory bulb, thousands of receptor-cell fibers (26,000 in the rabbit) synapse with about 100 second-order neurons, which then transmit the olfactory impulses to higher olfactory centers. Thus, there is a spatial summation in the neural impulses of about 260 to 1; this greatly increases the sensitivity of the system.

Thus, an olfactory receptor (1) is a primary sense cell, (2) has an extremely large adsorptive surface, (3) is in a neural system with great spatial summation. Even considering these structural advantages, the high degree of olfactory sensitivity remains incredible. De Vries and Stuiver (1961) have estimated the number of molecules stimulating the olfactory cells at the human absolute threshold. They used models of the nasal cavity to estimate how many odorous molecules in the inhaled air actually reach the sensory cells. After losses resulting from inhaled air bypassing the olfactory mucosa and from the adsorption of odorous molecules by the non-olfactory mucous membrane, only about 2 percent of the original inhaled molecules probably arrive to stimulate the sensory cells. The human threshold for mercaptans—such as skunk smell (one of the most powerful odorants for man)—is of the order of 10^9 inhaled molecules. The 2 percent estimate reduces this number to 2×10^7 molecules which reach the receptors. Since humans have about 4×10^7 receptor cells, at threshold, there is an average of about one mercaptan molecule for every two receptor cells. Allowing for some inaccuracy in the estimates, de Vries and Stuiver state that the human threshold for stimulating a single olfactory cell is, at most, 8 molecules.

Another way of visualizing this incredible sensitivity comes from research on musk, another powerful odorant. This substance, originally from the anal scent gland of the male musk deer but now produced synthetically, is used in extremely low concentrations as a perfume base. If the active ingredient of musk were spread on a film exposed to a continuous breeze, in one million years it would lose only about 1 percent of its potency as an odorant.

Most theories of olfactory functioning start with the need to describe a transduction process that is consistent with such data as that on musk—data indicating that minute amounts of energy initiate electrochemical changes. These theories are also based on two other types of data: (1) human psychophysical experiments to quantify the intensity dimension and to differentiate and classify the qualitative dimension; and (2) animal electrophysiological recordings from olfactory epithelia, sensory-cell nerve fibers, and various relevant places within the brain. Researchers who concentrate on either of these two types of data seek to find some orderly relations between the chemical or physical characteristics of the whole range of odorant stimuli and the neural patterning or sensations resulting from these stimuli. Without such orderly relations, it is difficult to understand how an odorant stimulates a receptor and how people are able to discriminate so many different odors. We shall briefly look at the psychophysical and electrophysiological data to see how they measure up in this respect.

Human psychophysical work on olfaction is beset with difficulties of standardizing the presentation of the stimulus. Since no way has been found to measure the extremely low odorant concentrations at the olfactory epithelium, the actual concentration and rate of flow past the receptors that occur with several stimulus-presentation techniques— normal breathing, sniffing, and a blast-injection method—may vary widely and lead to widely varying results. Many subjects are not able to respond consistently; even those that are require long training periods because they have little experience taking an analytical approach to olfactory sensations or guiding their responses by olfactory discriminations. Another problem is caused by the presence of cutaneous sensory receptors within the nasal cavity: touch, pain, warmth, and cold receptors. The simultaneous stimulation of these modalities often confounds judgments of "pure" odor.

Despite these problems, there have been a number of basic findings: (1) Absolute threshold levels, such as those already discussed for the mercaptans, have been obtained for many substances. (2) The ability to discriminate intensity differences has been studied extensively. In one study, trained subjects were able to identify only four different intensity levels of an odorant. (3) Stimuli consisting of more than one odorant have been used. When a mixture of two odorants is presented, the two generally fuse if they are similar, they may be smelled successively if they are dissimilar, or they may possibly cancel each other out. These effects may also be obtained when each nostril separately is stimulated with a different odorant. (4) Extensive data have also been obtained on the degree of adaptation to continuous stimulation by different odorants.

Many of these psychophysical findings have been applied to such problems as how the olfactory receptor cells work, whether individual receptors are differentially sensitive, and why particular chemical configurations are associated with particular odors. In trying to solve such problems, researchers generally ask their subjects to try to classify a wide range of odorants and then hope that the classification is related in some way to a chemical classification of the odorants. With six well-trained and consistent subjects, Henning (1924) was able to get some agreement on orderly relationships with over a hundred odorants. He used six substances (spicy, resinous, etherial, fragrant, burned, and putrid) as dividing points between eight qualitative continua. Another type of classification system used four basic odors (Crocker, 1945). Each sample was rated as to how much of each component it contained.

Unfortunately, no experimenter yet has discovered a psychological classification system which can be correlated with any single factor in the chemical makeup of the stimuli. Many schemes have been proposed that show a correlation for a portion of the odorant spectrum. So far, they always break down when extended; or someone discovers a stimulus with the right chemical structure but the wrong odor, or vice versa.

Thus, it is not surprising that the more fashionable place to look for such regularities today is in electrophysiological recording. As in the psychophysical data, one would hope to find receptor cells whose electrophysiological response is only to a single odorant or to some limited class of odorants with similar chemical properties. As we briefly review the electrophysiological data, the order of progression will be from the olfactory epithelium toward the higher-order neurons in the brain.

A one-second puff of mildly odorous air to the nasal cavity of a frog produces about a 5-millivolt negative potential that rises quickly and then decays in an exponential manner; the changes last about 4 seconds. This electrical change seems to originate in the finger-like processes at the top of the sensory cell. It has been called an electro-olfactogram (EOG) by Ottoson (1963), who considers it a summation of electrical activity in many receptor cells. Although this limits its usefulness for describing the sensitivity of single cells to different odorants, the EOG does show varying rise and decay rates with different stimuli. These different temporal patterns in the electrical response may provide some of the information that identifies different stimuli. They may also be related to the differences in the durations of olfactory sensations with different odorous stimuli as observed by humans.

More specific data on single cellular responses have recently been obtained by Gesteland (1963) from the nerve-fiber ends of the receptor cells. Because of the small diameter (0.2 mμ) of these fibers, the typical, very finely tipped (0.5 mμ) high-impedance microelectrodes could not be used to record the electrical potentials from the single fibers. Gesteland often was able to isolate the responses of single units with a larger ball-tipped electrode of low impedance when the electrode was inserted on an angle through the olfactory epithelium of the frog. Small puffs of mildly odorized air, blown directly on the olfactory epithelium, would typically produce a burst of spike potentials lasting 1 to 4 seconds. The major finding of this study of single nerve-fiber responses was the existence of patterns of odorant selectivity. When tested with 25 different odorants, each cell was found to be responsive to only some of them. Within the group of odors to which a cell was responsive, the size of the response would vary from odor to odor. Two cells with exactly the same set of response patterns were never found, but there was enough regularity to permit characterizing some eight different types of patterning. Unfortunately, the grouping of odorants within the eight types is not similar to any classification that can be made of either the chemical structure of Gesteland's stimuli or their resultant sensations as derived psychophysically in humans.

Gesteland discusses two explanations of the olfactory process which seem consistent with the data at this early stage. The first explanation posits several different types of olfactory receptor cells—types based on selective response properties. Under such a system one would expect to find cells of the same type responding in similar ways to all 25 odorants. This does not happen—perhaps because the theory is wrong, perhaps because the electrode tip introduced subtle changes in the cells. The second explanation posits different types of receptor sites distributed over each cell. The notion is that the part of a cell surface that is exposed to an odorant stimulus can contain many different sites, each sensitive in its own way. In such a system, each cell could respond uniquely, but one could still establish some grouping of fairly similar types of cells.

If we proceed on to the olfactory bulb, where the nerve fiber from the receptor cell has its first synapse with other neurons (see Figure 2), we find that the electrophysiological data become more complex. This increased complexity is typical of all afferent sensory pathways within the central nervous system. For the olfactory system, the complexity may be attributed to several anatomical features within the paired olfactory bulbs. There are abundant interconnections within each bulb and some fibers passing between them. Afferently evoked potentials in one bulb can be attenuated by strong stimulation to the other bulb. A large number of different fibers are also present, going from the limbic system to the olfactory bulbs. Thus, many central modulations of the incoming potentials may exist, or there may be feedback systems.

Two types of electrical potentials have been recorded in the bulb. Researchers using frogs have typically found spontaneous electrical waves with frequencies up to 100 per second—with no odorous stimulation. The frequency and amplitude of the waves is generally reduced at deep levels of anesthesia. With strong olfactory stimulation, electrical waves are recorded in the form of sinusoidal oscillations with frequencies between 10 and 60 per second, depending upon the level and type of anesthetic. If the anesthetic level diminishes the spontaneous activity, a strong odor stimulus may completely suppress it, leaving just the oscillatory electrical response.

The degree of specificity between a particular odor stimulus and the evoked electrical response in the bulb is not striking. There are differences in what is called the *wave envelope* of the electrical potentials (the latency, rise, and decay times for waves that are observable with several different odors). A greater degree of specificity is found in microelectrode recordings from single mitral cells, a type within the olfactory bulb. For any given odorant, the stimulus concentrations necessary to initiate a mitral-cell electrical response vary from cell to cell. Conversely, for any given mitral cell, the threshold will vary with different odorants. Although this type of specificity is quite similar to that found in the electrical response from the receptor cell, there is no indication at present of similar groupings of the odorous substances: The odorants which seem to have a similar electrical response at the level of the receptor cells do not cause similar effects in a mitral cell.

The olfactory bulb also seems to have regional sensitivities. As the recording electrode is moved in an antero-posterior direction, the size of the electrical response to the members of a set of odor stimuli changes. These changes correlate with some data on regional sensitivity differences on the surface of olfactory epithelium and an orderly anatomical arrangement of the nerve fibers from the epithelium to the bulb. Putting all these variables together, the discrimination of odors appears to be some function (1) of the detailed pattern of electrical discharges through time and (2) of the particular region that is maximally excited. Again, no obvious correlation has been found in either of these functions with psychophysical or chemical classifications of odorant substances.

The neural pathways from the olfactory bulb to higher brain centers have generally been described on the basis of evidence from techniques involving ablation, stimulation and electrical recording. Some 17 to 20 nuclei (areas), widely distributed throughout the brain, show anatomical or physiological evidence of having connections with the olfactory input from the bulb. They generally fall into two broad classifications. The axons of the mitral cells in the bulb pass in the olfactory stalk to the cerebral hemisphere and divide there into (1) a medial and (2) a lateral group. The medial group interconnects with taste impulses and is thereby related to feeding responses. Since many foods provide a greater smell than taste stimulus, this pathway permits the initiation or facilitation of muscle patterns for eating, swallowing, and peristalsis and also influences the output of the glands with salivary and digestive juices. By means of interconnections with auditory, visual, and tactual input pathways, branches from the medial group are involved in relating the sight, sound, and feel of food with its odor.

The lateral olfactory tract, in its connections with the hypothalamus and hippocampus by way of the amygdaloid nuclear group, functions primarily to correlate olfaction with a wide range of bodily processes.

When olfactory areas central to the olfactory bulb are selectively ablated or lesioned, simple conditioned responses to an odorous stimulus will generally be maintained. However, more complex conditioned reflexes, requiring a discrimination between two odors, can be abolished with bilateral removal of large areas in the olfactory portions of the forebrain.

We have briefly discussed the major sources of data on the olfactory system: the anatomical, electrophysiological, and psychophysical views of the events from stimulus to response. An appropriate summary statement seems to be that our knowledge of the workings of this system is rudimentary. As a result of the lack of correlation between the stimuli and the responses, between the energy properties of the odorant chemicals and the ways in which humans classify their odor sensations, countless theories have been devised to explain the nature of this process of stimulation. There are, among others, many infrared-radiation theories; many enzyme theories, wherein the odorant changes the catalyst balance or inhibits a reaction requiring a catalyst; and a theory requiring 24 different types of pigment molecules existing in an electronically excited state until de-excited by the relevant odorous molecule. The typical downfall of all these theories comes when some critic cites two substances which differ in the posited relevant stimulus property but smell the same to humans, or vice versa.

When theorists turn to the newer single-cell electrophysiological data and find the same lack of correspondence between typical chemical or psychophysical groupings and the grouping that can be made of the widely variable single-cell sensitivities, they can state only that discrimination is probably a complex matter. The theories suggest the possibility that the central nervous system supplements the individual receptor cell as a discriminator through the "use" of the patterning of responses from many different neural cells.

Some data of Ottoson's, the discoverer of the electro-olfactogram, illustrate the nature of the theory-making problem in olfaction. The voltage levels of the EOG were recorded when the receptors were presented with equimolar concentrations of alcohols in a series with an increasing number of carbon atoms. The results are shown in Figure 3. Here we see quite orderly relations between the number of carbon

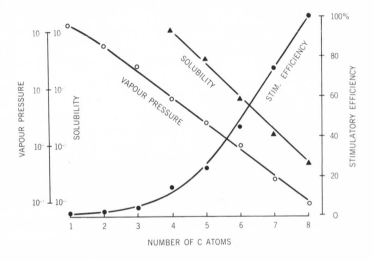

Figure 3

A line graph relating the number of carbon atoms to stimulating efficiency in terms of the voltage values in the EOG translated into percentage.

atoms and "stimulating efficiency" (a translation onto a percentage scale of the voltage values in the EOG). This orderly relation, especially since it occurs with several other organic compounds, could then form the basis of a theory of receptor functioning. However, the graph also indicates that two other variables, vapor pressure and solubility, show an orderly and direct relation with the number of carbon atoms and a high negative correlation with the stimulating efficiency. Thus, it is easy to see why theories have also been built by others around these two variables. Ottoson constructs his theory by combining all three aspects as they relate to thermodynamic activity. He concludes that substances of equal thermodynamic activity produce an equal stimulatory effect.

To reiterate, the field of olfaction still lacks much basic information. Accordingly, the sophistication of its theories suffers.

However, we can close our discussion of the sense of smell on an optimistic note, for research continues to yield fruitful and remarkable data. To illustrate, let's turn to an article by D. Schneider (1963), which follows the male Bombyx moth on the trail of his potential mate.

The olfactory receptors for a moth are located primarily in the antennae. An electrical potential can be recorded from an antenna; the voltage is related to the concentration of an odorous stimulus. The graph of this relationship, the *electroantennogram,* shows very little change in voltage at lower concentrations of odorous substances. This indicates that the male moth cannot make fine discriminations in the intensity of low concentrations; but the curve also indicates a great discrimination ability with higher concentrations.

Now, we place our male Bombyx a few hundred yards downwind of a female. Due to the distance over which it has diffused, the female odorant reaches him at a low concentration, but it is enough to initiate an upwind flight pattern. He meets many variations of the odorant concentration due to air turbulences, but he is unable to discriminate these differences, and his flight pattern remains straight upwind. When quite near to the waiting female, he reaches a stronger odorant concentration. With his great ability to discriminate among higher concentrations of the odorant, the male Bombyx can orient toward the female. The final touch in this story is that the concentration of the sex-attractant substance (bombykol!) in a female's bombykol gland, when dissected and used to stimulate an electroantennogram, produces voltage levels that correspond to those where fine discrimination seems plausible.

With that nice group of correspondences between behavioral, psychophysical, and electrophysiological data, we can leave the more typical confusions of smell and move on, without being unduly pessimistic, to some familiar and some not-so-familiar confusions in the study of taste.

TASTE

Anyone who is aware of the amount of work and creativity that goes into the preparation of a French gourmet dinner (or of typical dormitory fare?) may be surprised to learn that our tongues can only discriminate four basic tastes: sweet, sour, salty, and bitter. However—

before informing the chef that he's wasting his time—eat the meal and enjoy the many different subtle flavorings. Where's the discrepancy? What's the difference between the psychophysics of taste, with its four dull-sounding categories, and the marvellous sauces of the gourmet dinner?

The typical laboratory procedure uses as a stimulus a chemical compound such as sodium chloride dissolved to a given molar concentration (a measure of the number of molecules in 1,000 cc of distilled water), which is kept at a set temperature and flowed or dropped on a circumscribed area of a human's extended tongue. All olfactory cues are eliminated. With this type of procedure, the trained subject will be able to classify each of a wide variety of chemical compounds in terms of just the four dimensions: sweetness, sourness, saltiness, and bitterness. Occasionally, a study will add one or two more categories, but it's still not the gourmet dinner.

In the process of eating food, however, both the stimulus and the subject are in an entirely different state. Eating is an active process of placing, chewing, and swallowing. Both the mouth and the tongue are similar to the skin in being sensitive to pressure, temperature, pain, etc. Thus, what we naively think of as taste is confounded by the texture of the food and its temperature. The appearance of the food and the sounds of chewing are also influences. Perhaps most importantly, most foods that we consider appetizing stimulate our olfactory system. It is generally the olfactory system that makes the fine distinctions the French chef prides himself on. The olfactory system is capable of hundreds of qualitative discriminations, most of them with a much greater sensitivity than that for taste. As an example, the taste of acetic acid is indistinguishable from any other acid. It has a smell which is easily distinguished from other acids, and its olfactory threshold is 24,000 times lower than its taste threshold. You may have tried to eliminate the odor of foods by holding your nose, to see how the taste changes, and found very little difference. This is due partially to the greater olfactory sensitivity and partially to the existence of a back entrance to the olfactory epithelium going up from the mouth.

The lack of a threshold of sensitivity for taste comparable to that for smell is probably a result of the differences in their receptor cells. The olfactory receptor is a primary sensory cell combining the functions of transduction and conduction—the taste-receptor cell functions only as a transducer, making synaptic contact with branches from the first-order afferent neuron. However, these taste receptors are remarkable in their own way. The tongue has many small elevations called papillae closely scattered over its surface. Many of the papillae contain taste buds, each of which is made up of a number of receptor cells.

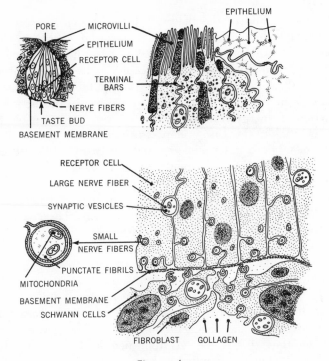

Figure 4

Diagram of the structure of a taste bud. (Redrawn from De Lorenzo, 1963.)

Figure 4, based on studies with the electron microscope, illustrates the finer structural details of these sensory cells. They contain finger-like extensions, the microvilli, which increase the surface area of the cell in a manner reminiscent of the olfactory cells. What is remarkable and unique about these taste cells is their average life span: between 3 to 5 days in the rat and rabbit and probably about the same in humans (Beidler, 1963).

What used to be described as different cell types within the taste buds has recently been shown to be different stages in growth and degeneration of each taste cell. New cells are continually forming at the periphery of the taste bud and migrating inward during maturation. This would seem to create a problem for the nerve fibers which have a synaptic contact with the cells. If we assume that a neuronal branch also migrates inward, there is the problem of its getting back up to the periphery after its receptor cell has degenerated. An alternative idea is that the maturing cell is passed from branch to branch as it migrates. This idea seems more likely, and it has fostered an interesting theory by Hallowell Davis (1963) which we shall look at in some detail.

The background of the theory is in the specific response patterns of individual taste receptors. These patterns of sensitivity have been recorded with a microelectrode inserted into the taste bud and are possibly electrical potentials from receptor cells in response to *sapid* substances (those having a taste). They are quite similar to the electrical potentials from olfactory epithelium, thus probably representing the transduction of energy from the chemical stimulus to an electrophysiological potential, in this case, a depolarization of the electrically charged taste-cell membrane. Each cell responds to many different sapid substances but the pattern of response varies from cell to cell. For example one cell may show a 9-millivolt response to a 0.1 molar concentration of NaCl and a 6-millivolt response to an equal concentration of sucrose. These same two stimuli presented to another cell could result in a 15-millivolt and a 0-millivolt response respectively. There are also some differences in sensitivity based on the topology of the tongue: Its tip is more sensitive to sweet and salt, its lateral margins to sour, its base to bitter, while its middle is insensitive to all tastes.

Now, back to the theory. If a newly formed taste cell starts with a given pattern of sensitivity, does it maintain this pattern through its period of maturation and degeneration? A "yes" answer would imply that as the migrating cell is passed from neuron to neuron, the set of messages conducted by an individual neuron would be dependent upon its particular cell mate for that day.

Microelectrode recording of the spike potentials from individual fibers in the nerve coming from the tip of the tongue, the chorda tympani nerve, unfortunately is of little assistance here. When chemicals representative of the four taste qualities are used as individual stimuli most cells respond to more than one. Different cells can be found with fairly similar "patterns" of sensitivity but they are not exactly alike. Researchers often compute these response patterns from the average number of spike potentials recorded during the first second after the chemical has been applied to the tongue.

With this type of information coming into the brain, the problem of discriminating one sapid substance from another would seem to be a function of the particular mixture of patterns arriving over specific fibers. When fibers A, B, and C are discharging with frequencies of 10, 20, and 30 spikes per second respectively, this would signal NaCl, whereas frequencies of 10, 10, and 10 would signal quinine (bitter). The important point in a discrimination system of this type is that the "meaning" of a particular signal is dependent upon both the discharge rate and the specific fiber that is discharging.

The idea of fiber specificity sets certain limits on the problems raised by the migration of the receptor cells from one neuron to another.

It gets us back to the question of whether the receptors, which also have specific patterns of sensitivity, can maintain their specificity unchanged while passing along the neurons. The logic of the situation seems to require that something has to give, either the neuron or the receptor. It seems more plausible to consider the neuron as the stable element in the system, since it is certainly more stable in its life span. We end up, then, with a system in which the specific sensitivity of receptor cells is changed according to the neural fiber or fibers with which it is in synaptic contact. The specificity of the individual neuron would be determined by its central connections in the brain and would remain constant.

This neural specificity must, then, act on the receptor with which it is in synaptic contact to change the receptor-cell specificity in conformance with its own specificity. There are indications, from continuous movie photographs of single neurons taken through a microscope, of a constant flow of chemicals originating at the cell body and passing along the axon within its tubular neurofibrils. The passage from the taste neuron to the taste-receptor cell of "information" governing changes in response specificity may depend upon such chemical streaming.

We have drawn a fairly complete picture of the observations and speculation that originate with the discovery of the taste receptor cells' short life span. It may be helpful to recapitulate the line of reasoning: (1) The receptor cells have a 3- to 5-day life span. (2) New cells form at the periphery of the taste bud and migrate towards its center. (3) Electrophysiological recording of the potential from single taste cells shows these cells sensitive to more than one basic substance, with different cells having different patterns of relative sensitivities. (4) Electrophysiological recording of the spike discharges from single neural fibers that synapse with the taste cells shows a specificity in terms of relative sensitivity to basic taste substances. (5) Assume that the migrating receptor cell changes its synaptic connections as it migrates. (6) Also assume that the specificity of the first-order neuron remains stable. (7) The simplest conclusion is that the specificity of the receptor cell is determined by the particular neurons it is synapsing with at a given time, and, thus, its specificity changes during its migration.

It shall be interesting to see the degree to which further data will support such a conclusion—or whether the whole notion will eventually be discarded. Meanwhile, the proposed system has renewed interest in the physiology of taste and provided some grounds for fascinating speculation about what seems to be a unique dynamic system in the body. It also raises additional problems in conducting experiments and interpreting results, as a given taste receptor cell can no longer be considered a stable element through time.

Aside from the unusualness of the problems raised by a rapid turn-over of taste cells, there is a possibility of its relevance for one of the major phenomena in taste-initiated behavior: preference and self-se-lection. Much of the behavioral work on taste with animals has involved testing for taste preferences and permitting a cafeteria-style self-selec-tion of foods. In a typical procedure, the animal is trained to sample and drink from two drinking tubes providing the same liquid. After it learns to drink from both about equally, the solution in one container is changed, then the changed solution is shifted randomly from the left to the right side. The relative amounts of the two solutions consumed is a measure of the animal's preference. Such experiments have been an extremely useful tool for understanding the factors involved in accep-tance or rejection of food substances.

In 1942, C. P. Richter reported his now classic studies of self-selection in rats which demonstrated their ability to compensate for nutritive, endocrine, and vitamin deficiencies by changing their eat-ing patterns. One of the results of removal of the adrenal glands is a sodium deficiency which soon leads to death. Richter found that adrenalectomized rats, when given the opportunity, will increase their salt intake enough to completely compensate for their deficiency. If a preference-testing situation is used, the adrenalectomized rat shows a lowered threshold for NaCl detection and will accept NaCl solutions at high concentrations that were previously rejected. His findings were similar with calcium and Vitamin A deficiencies.

With over a twenty years' follow-up of Richter's experiments, there are abundant data for many of the questions concerning the means by which these thresholds and preferences may be shifted to maintain proper dietary intake. Both electrophysiological recording and condi-tioning studies have demonstrated a lack of change in the sensitivity of taste receptors after adrenalectomy and also after insulin injection (which leads to a greatly increased sugar intake). The taste cells are a necessary part of the self-selection phenomena, however. If the neural pathway from the receptors is cut, the increased NaCl intake of the adrenalectomized rat does not take place. Thus it would appear that taste must be a factor, but since taste sensitivity doesn't change, some-thing else must be involved which does show changes.

Two interesting techniques have been used to assess the influence of the stomach on factors relative to taste. One technique, called an esophageal fistula, prevents the ingested food or liquid from reaching the stomach; a reverse procedure, loading of the stomach through a tube, prevents any taste sensations. A salt-deficient rat with an esophageal fistula will maintain its increased salt intake and modified threshold for preference; a rat whose stomach is loaded with salt solution through a tube will proportionately decrease the salt taken by mouth so that the combined volume is enough to compensate for the deficiency. The general conclusion drawn from these two experimental procedures is that both taste and what may be called post-ingestion factors (intragastric or metabolic) influence the drinking behavior.

Many further refinements and variations of these basic procedures have been applied to this type of problem. Short 10-minute preference testing has been substituted for the typical 24-hour periods in order to reduce post-ingestion factors; an "electronic esophagus" which is a combination of an esophageal fistula and a device to continuously record the licking rate, allows the experimenter to have a rat drink one solution while an equal volume of another solution is automatically introduced into its stomach via a tube; various solutions to provide bulk or change the physiological osmotic pressure while keeping taste factors constant, or vice versa, have been utilized with several types of diet-induced or surgically induced metabolic deficiencies.

The results of each additional study indicate that while the problem of relating preference and ingestion behavior to taste, metabolic, osmotic, and stomach-loading factors is a complex one, an explanation in which all these variables play important roles seems inescapable.

The question now becomes one of understanding how the individual variables operate in the manner they do to influence the ingestion and preference behavior. Especially intriguing is the mechanism whereby taste reflects metabolic shifts. This is where we get back to the earlier discussion of the short life span of taste-receptor cells and their continual replacement. When this discovery was made, it seemed to provide an easy mechanism whereby changing preference thresholds could result from a metabolic or dietary deficiency; the argument ran: When the division of epithelial cells and their development into taste cells occurred under a given metabolic deficiency, it resulted in a different level of threshold sensitivity for the deficient substance.

We have seen, however, that the neural response coming directly from the taste cells indicates a lack of any changes in taste-cell sensitivity. These experiments have been carefully repeated without any change in the primary conclusion. It looks like nutritional deficiencies must have some other way of influencing taste.

One suggestion, with some supporting data, concerns the role of saliva as an adapting background for taste sensation. McBurney and Pfaffmann (1963) found that the human threshold sensitivity for NaCl detection was between 100 and 1,000 times more sensitive when the tongue had been continually bathed with distilled water rather than its typical moistening of saliva. Further experiments, with weak NaCl solutions as the adapting background (the continuous before-and-after bath), demonstrated a high positive correlation between the detection threshold and the NaCl concentration in the adapting solution.

It is known that the NaCl content of saliva, as well as its other constituents, is a reflection of the concentrations of these substances in the blood. Thus, McBurney and Pfaffmann see the dietary deficiency being reflected in the blood and shifting the chemical makeup of the saliva. This changes it as an adapting background; the "neutral" point against which substances are detected or discriminated is shifted. The end result is the sought-after mechanism for obtaining taste-threshold shifts that reflect metabolic deficiencies, without a change taking place in the taste cell itself.

Although this is an attractive explanation for shifts in detection threshold following such things as adrenalectomy, it doesn't necessarily explain such shifts in preference behavior as the increased intake of NaCl. Here, the evidence seems to point to post-ingestion factors as the most important variable. This implies that there is some means whereby the ability of a substance to correct for a deficiency, its post-ingestion activity, is correlated with a shift in preference toward that substance. Thus, taste is regarded as important only to identify the substance that, by reducing a bodily need, becomes more desirable.

Organisms seem to be doubly protected for maintaining a proper intake of food substances. The preference for the needed substance increases along with the ability to detect the substance. There are some interesting examples of these compensatory processes in both humans and animals. Native women in the West Indies, when they become pregnant, eat the chalk that they normally use to chalk their looms. There is a famous salt lick in the Royal Game Park in Kenya to which herbivorous animals travel many miles. Plant food is quite deficient in sodium salts but has a sufficient amount of potassium salts. Humans find it quite difficult to discriminate sodium salts from potassium salts. The herbivorous animal with a sodium deficiency has no such difficulty. Self-selection and preference behavior are not foolproof, however. Such things as a craving for sweets are often not related in any way to a metabolic need as many overweight people and some diabetics know only too well.

Much less is known about mechanisms by which stomach loading via a tube influences preference behavior. We have probably all experienced that stage in packing away a huge meal when it seems impossible to swallow any more food. The slow-down warnings seem to come from the stomach. About the only relevant experimental data concern the anatomy of the pathways that may create these warnings. The incoming taste pathways travel in three cranial nerves: Part of the seventh cranial nerve comes from the anterior portion of the tongue, the ninth from the posterior portion and the tenth from the larynx and pharynx. All three enter the medulla of the brainstem and have pathways ascending to the arcuate nucleus of the thalamus. From there they project to the same areas of the surface of the cerebral cortex receiving cutaneous sensations from the face, the area by the lower end of the central fissure. It is in the arcuate nucleus that the stomach-loading phenomenon probably has its anatomical basis. Recent Russian work has demonstrated the existence of neural pathways going from receptors in the stomach lining up to the arcuate nucleus. Experiments still remain to be done studying the effects of tube loading of the stomach on preference testing with these pathways cut.

There is a great deal more data on taste processes that we are not able to include here. The large body of data on the specifics of the stimuli that evoke sweet, sour, salty and bitter sensations has been neglected as have the many experiments on absolute and differential thresholds and adaptation effects. However, since this chapter on chemical sensitivity started by emphasizing the importance of this sensory modality in human behavior, it seems appropriate to end with a quotation from the end of a treatise, written in 1825, on the "Physiology of Taste," by Jean Anthelme Brillat-Savarin, the famous gastronome.

AN HISTORICAL ELEGY

First parents of mankind, whose gourmandism is
historical, ye who lost all for an apple, what would
you not have done for a truffled turkey? But in the
earthly paradise were neither cooks nor confectioners:

How I pity you

Great kings who laid proud *Troy* in ruins, your
valour will go down from age to age; but your table
was wretched. Reduced to ox-thighs and the backs
of swine, you never knew the charms of *matelote*,
no, nor the bliss of chicken fricassee:

How I pity you

Chloe, Aspasio, and ye all whom Grecian chisels
made eternal for the despair of all our beauties
of to-day, never did your bewitching mouths draw
in the suavity of rose nor vanilla meringue; you
scarcely even rose to gingerbread:

How I pity you

Roman financiers, who squeezed the known
world dry of gold, your famous banquet-halls
ne'er saw our many-flavoured ices, cold to
brave the torrid zone, nor yet our jellies which
are joy in idleness:

How I pity you

Unconquerable paladins, made famous in the songs
of troubadors, alas when you had smitten giants
hip and thigh, set damsels free, and wiped out
armies utterly, no blackeyed captive maid ere
brought you sparkling champagne, Madeira
malvoisie, nor liqueurs, the pride of the grand
century; you were reduced to ale or sour herb-
flavoured wine:

How I pity you

And you, too, gastronomes of 1825, sated in the
bosom of plenty, and already dreaming of new
dishes, not for you the mysteries science shall
reveal in 1900, mineral esculences perchance, or
liqueurs distilled from an hundred atmospheres;
not yours to see what travellers yet unborn shall
bring from that half of the globe which still remains
to be discovered or explored:

How I pity you

Perhaps you would like to write a final verse on TV dinners.

REFERENCES

Beidler, L. M. Dynamics of taste cells. In Y. Zotterman (Ed.), *Olfaction and taste*. New York: MacMillan, 1963.

Crocker, E. C. *Flavor*. New York: McGraw-Hill, 1945.

Davis, H. Discussion (to Beidler, 1963). In Y. Zotterman (Ed.), *Olfaction and taste*. New York: MacMillan, 1963.

De Lorenzo, A. J. Studies on the ultrastructure and histophysiology of cell membranes, nerve fibers and synaptic junctions in chemo-receptors. In Y. Zotterman (Ed.), *Olfaction and taste*. New York: MacMillan, 1963.

De Vries, H., and Stuiver, M. The absolute sensitivity of the human sense of smell. In W. A. Rosenblith (Ed.), *Sensory communication*. New York: John Wiley, 1961.

Gesteland, H. C., et al. Odor specificities of the frog's olfactory receptors. In Y. Zotterman (Ed.), *Olfaction and taste*. New York: MacMillan, 1963.

Henning, H. *Der Geruch*. Leipzig: Barth, 1924.

McBurney, D. H., and Pfaffmann, C. Gustatory adaptation to saliva and sodium chloride. *J. expl. Psychol.*, 1963, 523.

Ottoson, D. Generation and transmission of signals in the olfactory system. In Y. Zotterman (Ed.), *Olfaction and taste*. New York: Macmillan, 1963.

Parkes, A. S., and Bruce, H. M. Olfactory stimuli in mammalian reproduction. *Science*, 1961, *134*, 1049–1054.

Richter, C. P. Total self-regulatory functions in animals and human beings. *Harvey Lect.*, 1943, 38, 36–103.

Schneider, D. Electrophysiological investigation of insect olfaction. In Y. Zotterman (Ed.), *Olfaction and taste*. New York: Macmillan, 1963.

ADDITIONAL REFERENCES

Amore, J. E., Johnston, J. W., and Rubin, The stereochemical theory of odor. *Sci. Amer.*, 1964.

Beidler, L. M. The chemical senses. *Ann. Rev. Psychol.*, 1963, *12*, 263–388.

Kare, M. R., and Halpern, B. P. (Eds.). *Physiological and behavioral aspects of taste*. Chicago: University of Chicago Press, 1961.

Pfaffmann, C. Sensory processes and their relation to behavior: Studies on the sense of taste as a model S-R system. In Koch, S. (Ed.), *Psychology, a study of a science*, Vol. IV. New York: McGraw-Hill, 1962.

THE INTERNAL ENVIRONMENT
David Wolsk

5

INTRODUCTION

Holding one's breath is a popular sport for kids. I would like the reader to try it as a start toward understanding the problems of research on internal sensations. As you hold your breath, there is a growing sense of—what? Try concentrating on the experience. You may be feeling such things as an increasing desire or pressure to deflate the lungs, occasional muscle contractions in the throat and diaphragm, tension changing to pain around the throat and upper chest, emptiness and discomfort in the stomach. It is not easy to describe your situation—to find just the right words to communicate the sensations that originate in the internal environment.

Now for another demonstration: Close your eyes and put your hand somewhere in front of you. With your eyes still closed, you can describe where your hand is and, with your other hand, be accurate in touching it. But try to report *how* you know its position.

In 1826, Charles Bell, an English physiologist, described a woman with an insensitive arm who could hold her baby to her breast only while she was looking at the arm. If she looked away, her arm dropped, and the baby fell. Because the neural pathway—coming from receptors that normally signals the arm's position—was damaged, she could control her arm only by watching it.

Bell's paper is a landmark in a continuing discussion of the nature of input to the nervous system from within the body and from without— that is, from *intero-receptors* and from *extero-receptors*. The two demonstrations with which we began this chapter are intended to show that stimulation from inside the body is generally less distinct than stimulation from outside the body. This difference is important in the experimental study of sensory processes. It is the difference between (1) asking a subject to press a button whenever the second of two tones sounds louder than the first, and (2) asking him to press a button whenever the "position sense" from his left arm is more intense than from his right.

It would be a dubious undertaking to base an experimental science on the descriptions of what people feel when they hold their breath or on descriptions of the intensity of their position sense. In a discussion of internal sensations, E. G. Boring listed eleven sensory qualities which had been seriously studied (thirst, hunger, appetite, stomach emptiness, stomach repletion, nausea, excretory needs and processes, sexual needs and processes, dizziness, cardiac oppression, and suffocation). Boring prefaced the list by calling it an epitaph, in the hope that twentieth-century psychology had finally laid to rest the nineteenth-century search for a "sensory quality" to accompany every bodily function.

Although his list has remained in its final resting place, with only fitful rumblings, psychology has accomplished very little toward devising an acceptable replacement. Thus this chapter will tend more to express a personal viewpoint toward the phenomena of the internal environment than to summarize widely accepted approaches to a standard set of problems and data as previous chapters have done.

The general premise of this chapter is that it is fruitful to consider the information received in the brain from intero-receptors as a framework or background for the input we receive from the external environment. This "background" information concerns both the position and movement of our body and its physiological state—from the osmotic pressure in the tissues to the level of sex hormones in the blood, from an "ants-in-the-pants" feeling after an hour of studying to "butterflies in the stomach" as an exam is passed out. The background has three major influences on the external output: (1) It serves to direct attention—to govern the process of selection by which we attend to only a small portion of the information available to our eyes, ears, nose, etc. (2) It serves to distinguish movements of the organism from movements in the surrounding environment. (3) It serves to modify the significance of the external input by adding to it an emotional quality. Thus, an organism with a high level of circulating sex hormones (1) may direct it's attention toward organisms of the opposite sex; (2) may successfully pursue such an organism even if it is retreating; and (3) may have positive emotional reactions to the sight, smell, and sound of the potential mate.

How does background information arise? At the human level, we can identify two types of input from the intero-receptors. The first type identifies movements of one's own head and body. This type consists of signals from the vestibular system (concerning the position and movements of the head) combined with signals from joints (about other bodily movements). Against this background, movements of the retinal image can be separated into movements of the organism and movements outside the organism. The second type of input originates in the visceral receptors. Input from the viscera signals the level of many physiological variables and provides a broad background for vision, audition, smell, and taste.

While input from the vestibular organs and joints is closely allied to the motoric activity of the organism, the visceral input relates more to the affective aspect of activity (the feelings or "emotional loading" attached to the stimuli) and to selection and attention (in the motivational and sensory filtering processes).

One interesting difference between the extero-receptors and the intero-receptors lies in their time scales—in the rapidity with which they typically operate. The time scale for the majority of sensory processing from the extero-receptors is relatively short. Once we have seen, heard, smelled, or tasted something, we quickly move on. Specialization for rapid changes diminishes the ability of these sensory modalities to perceive slow changes. At twilight we are often surprised to suddenly realize how dark it has become. Try to imagine what music would be like if it were slowed down considerably. There must be some point at which music ceases to be music when slowed down enough. If we are placed in an unchanging visual, auditory, or olfactory environment, we soon adapt to the stimulation that is present and become unaware of it or even unable to perceive it. Thus, the color in a completely uniform visual field (a *Ganzfeld*) rapidly fades away. Such rapid adaptations in the extero-receptive systems are a blessing for those who work in a cow barn or near an air-conditioning machine.

On the other hand, the receptors within our external organs signal slow changes in the steady-state levels of the particular variables to which they are sensitive. We don't suddenly become hungry or satiated; changes in blood pressure are sometimes relatively fast, but still not as fast as the flick of an eye; the levels of hormones in the blood stream do not undergo rapid changes. One can cite instances of rapid responses to rapid events within the organism, especially to pain and changes in the adrenalin level, but the typical mode of action for intero-receptive systems is slow: seconds, minutes, and hours are involved, rather than the milliseconds and seconds of the external receptive systems.

This difference in time scale is, perhaps, one of the reasons for the comparative lack of research on intero-receptive sensory processes. In a typical experiment with extero-receptors, a short stimulus is repeatedly presented and the immediate responses are measured. The intero-receptors are not easy to stimulate repeatedly in a uniform manner, and measurable responses often come slowly and last long. However difficult the research may be, and whatever new approaches are needed, the study of internal sensations seems worth the effort. While it is obvious that input from the intero-receptors is not as rich in information as visual and auditory output, still, the degree to which an organism's over-all behavior is determined by its internal environment is quite high.

Unfortunately, with the paucity of research, there is no obvious way of presenting a logical and orderly coverage of bodily orientation and the internal environment as they relate to ongoing behavior. About all that seems possible, within the limits of the present state of the data and theories of the allotted space, is to describe (1) receptors and their transduction processes, (2) incoming neural pathways, and (3) tieups that have occasionally been observed between the internal environment and behavioral phenomena.

In this chapter, we will describe the vestibular and kinesthetic systems involved in maintaining bodily orientation as well as sensations in various internal organs.

BODILY ORIENTATION

All multicellular organisms generally maintain a particular orientation toward gravity. That this usually requires an active process of balancing is illustrated by the belly-up position of dead fish. An organism must also monitor its own movements and know the relative position of the different parts of its body. Most organisms possess a large number of complex receptor systems to serve these functions. All of these receptor cells require a mechanical deformation; they are called mechanoreceptors. In man, the mechanoreceptors for bodily orientation are located in tendons, muscles and joint capsules, and within the temporal bone on the side of his skull.

THE VESTIBULAR SYSTEM

Within the same bony cavity that contains the inner ear, there is a structure called the *vestibular apparatus*. It consists of three semicircular canals, a *utricle*, and a *saccule*, all interconnected. Figure 1 illustrates some

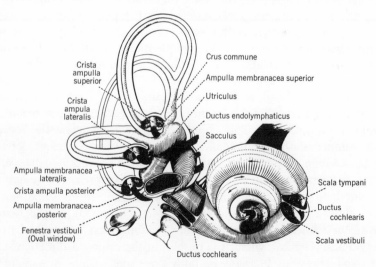

Figure 1

The structure of the semicircular canals.

of its main details, especially the close relationship of the vestibular apparatus with the inner ear. Each semicircular canal has an enlarged end containing receptor cells and fine terminal branches of the vestibular nerve. These receptor cells within each semicircular canal are so arranged that they undergo a mechanical deformation whenever the head is subjected to an angular or rotatory acceleration or deceleration.

The top of each receptor cell has a number of hairs embedded in a tissue mass that covers the receptor tissue. This mass is called the cupula, and it looks and acts like a swinging door having its hinged side by the hair cells. When the head is rotated, the receptor cells move with it as they are attached to the bony canal wall, but the canal fluid lags behind due to its inertia—pushing the "swinging door" and thereby pulling on the hairs and stimulating the receptor cells. If a constant rotatory motion is maintained, the frictional force between the fluid and the canal walls overcomes the inertia so that both fluid and receptor cells are moving at the same speed. The "swinging door," acting as if it were spring loaded, slowly moves back to a neutral position so that the receptor cells are no longer stimulated. Behaviorally, we are unaware of constant-speed rotary motion if all visual and vibration cues are eliminated.

This is a somewhat simplified account of a process that is not fully understood. Two important aspects of its functioning, however, can be understood. First, the planes in which the three semicircular canals are arranged are at right angles to each other like the three planes that meet in the corner of a room. Since the maximal stimulation to a single canal— the greatest amount of lag between the fluid and the receptor cells— occurs when the rotatory acceleration is in the plane of that canal, the right-angle of orientation of the three canals is the best geometric solution for maximum sensitivity in all possible planes of rotation. The second important point also relates to the problem of sensitivity: At the base of each receptor cell are synaptic junctions with the neurons of the vestibular nerve. When the head is not moving, the majority of these neurons discharge spontaneously with a quite even rate (about 70 per second) in the guinea pig and frog. This impulse rate is varied when the receptor cell is stimulated. Depending on the direction of mechanical deformation, the change in the electrical potential of the receptor cell is either positive or negative. This change acts, in some manner that is not well understood, to increase the spontaneous discharge rate of some neurons and to decrease the rate of others. About 83 percent of the neurons increase their discharge rate when the "swinging door" is pushed in one direction and decrease when it is pushed in the opposite direction. Some 12 percent show an increase in both directions, while 5 percent are inhibited in both directions (Gernandt, 1949). Such a system of signaling changes has a dual advantage: (1) Since the nerve cells are already spontaneously discharging, there is no neural threshold to overcome. (2) Each cell can signal two directions of rotation by either increasing or decreasing the spontaneous discharge rate.

In achieving a maximal sensitivity for rotatory acceleration, the semicircular-canal part of the vestibular system sacrifices its sensitivity to linear acceleration. Head movements in a straight line cannot result in a lag in the motion of the canal fluid relative to the receptor tissue. Receptor cells in the utricle and the saccule, however, operating under similar principles of the energy of inertia and gravity but within a different physical arrangement, are stimulated by accelerative motion in a straight line.

The receptor cells in the utricle and saccule are arranged as a fairly flat sheet of tissue and are structurally quite similar to the receptors of the semicircular canals, containing hairs at one end and synaptic connections with branched fibers from the vestibular nerve at the other end. The key part of this system is a sheet of tissue called the *otolithic membrane,* which lies over the hair-bearing end of the receptor-cell sheet.

Two features of the otolithic membrane explain its functioning: (1) It consists largely of dense crystals of calcium carbonate, which make it quite a bit heavier than the receptor tissue underneath. (2) It is free to move slightly when pulled by the force of gravity, while the receptors remain fixed to their bony surround. When it is pulled by gravity, the position of the otolithic membrane relative to the receptor cells is determined by the position of the head. When the head is in its usual upright position, the sheet of receptor-cell tissue in the utricle lies horizontally and the otolithic membrane is directly above it so that its weight is applied at a right angle to the receptor tissue. A forward tilt of the head will shift the angle at which the force of gravity is pulling the otolithic membrane. Since the receptor cells are fixed in place while the otolithic membrane is not, this membrane will slide slightly forward, thereby applying a mechanical force to the hairs of the receptor cells. The bending or tilting of these hairs is, presently, our best guess as to the actual mechanical stimulation of the receptors. If, instead of tilting, the head is accelerated in a straight line, a similar shifting of the otolithic membrane relative to the receptor takes place—this is due to the inertia of the unattached otolithic membrane, which causes it to lag behind the attached receptor tissue. The utricle, oriented in a horizontal plane, is most sensitive to horizontal linear acceleration; the saccule, oriented vertically, responds best to up-and-down motion.

It should be apparent that a centrifugal force from rotatory motion will also shift the otolithic membrane. Why, then, do we need semicircular canals? The advantage of the semicircular canal system for signaling rotation is one of sensitivity. Because the utricle and the saccule are close to the center of the head, they are subject to very little centrifugal force with normal head movements. Thus, much greater sensitivity is achieved by the addition of the receptor system within the canals, where inertial force provides the stimulation.

Recordings have been made in several different animals of the electrical activity of the afferent fibers that synapse at the base of the receptor cells in the utricle and saccule. When the head is tilted to one side, the impulse frequency from the utricle typically increases on that side and shows no change on the opposite side. Experimenters have obtained an increased impulse rate from an implanted electrode during a cat's free fall. A free fall primarily affects the saccule.

Now that you have a rudimentary notion of the structure and functioning of the receptors in the vestibular system, it is possible to look at the very complex things that happen to this neural input within the central nervous system. What aspects of behavior are influenced by the vestibular input?

One of the best demonstrations of the beautiful functioning of this system is something you may have tried with one of your neighbor's cats. A cat, suspended upside down by its feet and then released, will manage to right itself and land on its feet. One of the first scientific applications of the movie camera was to photograph this sequence. When the film was presented to the French Academy of Sciences in 1894, it aroused a storm of controversy. The physicists, secure in their knowledge that for every action there is an equal and opposite reaction, called the whole idea impossible. If the head end started twisting in one direction, the hind end must twist oppositely, and the only result could be an unhappy cat. Fortunately for the cat, some French mathematicians achieved a solution which was satisfactory to all of the participants. They showed how the force for the cat's half-circle turn could be derived from the changing arc of its body. The mathematical derivation is quite complex. It took mathematicians a long time to justify what the cat does automatically in less than a second. It is clearly the vestibular system alone that performs this bodily orientation in mid-air. A cat whose vestibular organs have been destroyed lands in a heap when it is dropped. But a normal cat, dropped even in the dark, lands on its feet.

Observe the multitude of changes in the position of the legs and body of a dog when it moves its head from sniffing on the ground to sniffing something held high in front of it. Much of the coordination for postural movements utilizes vestibular input, especially where movement is initiated by changes in head position.

The neural pathways involved in these reflexes are shown in Figure 2; some descend to synapse on the motor neurons of the spinal cord, or go to the cerebellum. The term *equilibrium* refers to this set of reflexes which maintains normal body position both at rest and during motion.

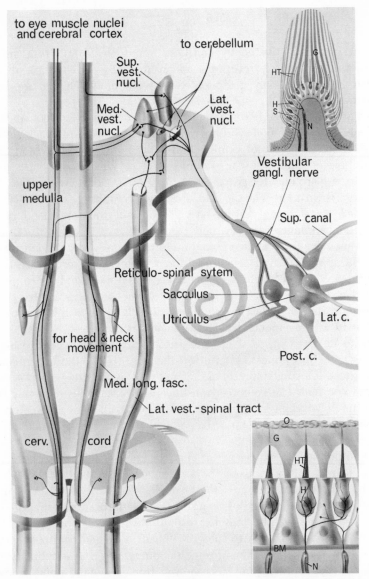

Figure 2

Neural pathways from the vestibular system. The inset diagram above shows a crista acoustica, the type of sensory structure found in the semicircular canals. The hair tufts (HT) occur in a gelatinous substance (G). They arise from hair cells (H) which are situated next to supporting cells (S). Nerve fibers (N) are connected to the hair cells. The lower inset shows part of a macula acoustica, the type of sensory structure found in both the saccula and utricle. In a macula, the otoconia (O) lies on a gelatinous layer (G). The nerve fibers are shown passing through a basilar membrane (BM).

The reflexes are activated by vestibular input plus input from the skin, from joints and muscle receptors, and from the eyes. They are all inter-related in an extremely complicated network of which we are largely ignorant.

If you have ever found yourself with an overly high concentration of alcohol in your blood, you are probably well aware of the benefits of a well-functioning set of equilibrium reflexes. The best demonstration of this role of the vestibular system has come from experiments under-taken to prepare men for space flight. At the Pensacola Naval Base, there is a large room placed at the end of a huge rotating beam. The room is furnished for sleeping, eating, etc. A constant rotation speed of 5-10 revolutions a minute creates a new constant line of force on the otolithic membrane—this force is a combination of the usual vertical gravity vector plus the new horizontal centrifugal-force vector. The results are at first rather devastating on volunteers who live in the room and try to perform manual tasks. Trying to walk in a straight line produces a curved path; throwing a dart at a dart board results in a large miss to one side; any sudden head movements produce immediate dizziness. All the subject wants to do is to go to sleep, but turning over in his sleep brings on another spell of dizziness. After a few days of this life, the brain seems to make some adjustments in its circuitry, as all aspects of behavior slowly return to normal. The volunteer must eventually leave his revolving room. Unfortunately, when he does, the ordeal starts all over again, but in a reversed direction; e.g., the darts now land on the opposite side of the target.

Another major experimental method for vestibular studies makes use of neural pathways from the vestibular system to the extrinsic eye muscles, those which rotate the eyeball. Figure 2 shows the neural pathways (from the vestibular nuclei to the three nuclei in the brain stem) which control the muscles responsible for eye movements. These pathways serve primarily to integrate head movements with eye move-ments, thus providing the information on which a distinction can be made between stationary objects viewed from a moving point of regard and moving objects viewed while stationary. Since eye movements are also under voluntary control, it is often difficult to separate the vestibular from the voluntary control mechanisms. A major amount of the informa-tion we have concerning the stimulus-response relationships for angular and linear acceleration has been solely derived from the duration or speed of the resulting back-and-forth *nystagmus* movements of the eyes. You can observe this nystagmus movement by spinning someone in a rotating chair and then quickly stopping the rotation. Unfortunately, nystagmus leaves much to be desired as a primary dependent variable, but this is part of the difficulty of studying a sensory system which has no conscious referent.

Beside the postural and eye-movement effects, another important set of responses is initiated by stimulation of vestibular receptors: the motion sickness (carsickness, seasickness, airsickness) that results from overstimulation or unusual stimulation. Motion sickness can be produced in a laboratory by rapid acceleration and deceleration of a spinning chair. For most people, the effect is a feeling of dizziness and nausea. The remarkable thing about the nausea connected with motion sickness is the length of time it lasts. One minute of overstimulation can make a person miserable for a full day. An anatomical pathway—from the vestibular nuclei to the reticular substance and then to the vagus nerve innervating the smooth muscle of the stomach—explains how the stomach gets affected (see Figure 2). But a satisfactory explanation for both the duration of this effect and its possible significance or derivation is lacking. Since a cat can be rapidly accelerated and decelerated in a spinning apparatus for hours without any obvious signs of distress, one may well wonder of motion sickness: Who needs it? (A cat may get sick if linear acceleration in a vertical plane is used as the stimulus.)

Fortunately, those whose occupations require overstimulation to the vestibular receptors are generally able to suppress the usual effects. One of the more remarkable examples of this suppression occurs in figure skaters, who decelerate extremely rapidly from a spin which may hit a speed of almost eight revolutions a second and are able to skate away in a straight line with no loss of form, no dizziness, and, most surprising, no nystagmus. Animal research is in progress to determine whether this slowly acquired suppression utilizes efferent neuronal pathways which go from the brain stem to synapse at the base of the vestibular receptors.

The existence of such efferent paths adds one more complicating factor to a system that already taxes reseachers' comprehension and ingenuity. The vestibular apparatus is an almost inaccessible organ, of minute dimensions, whose neural input has no conscious component, and whose behavioral responses to stimulation are quite difficult to work with. Thus, while our knowledge of the receptor anatomy and the peripheral electrophysiology is quite good, and we appreciate its central role in maintaining equilibrium and postural reflexes and in differentiating environmental movement from head movement, the underlying mechanisms of the central nervous system remain largely unexplored.

TOUCH AND KINESTHESIS

The other major systems that provide information about the orientation and movements of the body are touch and kinesthesis. For touch, the stimuli are ones which deform the skin or move the hairs it contains. Kinesthetic stimuli displace or deform the tissue underlying the skin: the connective tissue, bones, tendons, and the capsules of joints. The term kinesthesis, derived from the Greek word for motion, *kinesis,* reflects the primary connection of this sensory system with changes in the length of muscles. We are considering touch and kinesthesis together because their primary relationship to behavior is often quite similar, and the neural inputs from both sets of receptors travel quite closely together, synapsing in the same regions and arriving at about the same place in the cerebral cortex. Also, the transduction process for both touch and kinesthesis is a change from mechanical to electrical energy.

Experimenters face the as yet unsolved problem of devising the means for precise quantitative control of mechanical stimulation within an intact organism. Thus many recent data on the transduction process have been obtained by dissecting out individual receptors for precise study.

The receptors for touch and kinesthesis consist of free (bare) nerve endings and a variety of encapsulations of nerve endings (Pacinian corpuscle, Meissner's corpuscle, Ruffini's endings). While each of these capsules was previously thought to be structurally distinct and sensitive to only one type of stimulus (cold, pain, pressure, etc.), more recent anatomical and electrophysiological studies by a group at Oxford University have challenged these views. They dispute the classification of the capsules, maintaining that many of them are structurally intermediate between all of the previously described "types." The Oxford researchers further are unable to substantiate the idea that there are specific types of capsules sensitive to specific stimulus modalities. Behaviorally, they find that stimulation of the cornea can produce all modalities of sensation despite the presence there of just free nerve endings.

However, recordings made of the electrical activity from the cutaneous nerves show that certain receptors are extremely sensitive to mechanical deformation and are not easily excited by thermal or chemical stimuli. Thus, despite the full spectrum of sensitivity in the cornea and the confused anatomical picture, there are data pointing to some specificity on the part of given receptors.

The most widely studied type of mechanoreceptor is the Pacinian corpuscle, found in the skin, muscles, tendons, and joints. The structure of this unit and the experimental setup used by Lowenstein for studying its electrophysiological responses are illustrated in Figure 3. The onion-like structure, about 0.02–0.06 inch in length and consisting of alternate cellular and fluid layers, transmits a deformation to the unmyelinated nerve ending in the center. A receptor electrical potential is produced which reflects both the amount and velocity of the displacement. When the voltage of this potential reaches a certain level, it spreads to the myelinated portion of the neuron, triggering a neural impulse (Lowenstein, 1960). The Pacinian corpuscle is quite a sensitive transducer: A move-

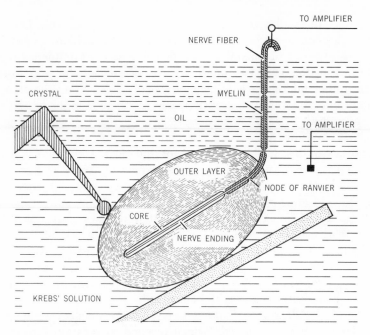

Figure 3

An isolated Pacinian corpuscle in the arrangement used to study its functioning. It is mechanically stimulated by the rod from the vibrating crystal. The resulting nerve impulses are recorded by the electrodes. (Copyright © 1960 by Scientific American, Inc. All rights reserved.)

ment of about .0001 inch is all the stimulation necessary to excite this receptor.

The receptors for touch and kinesthesis fall into two broad classes based on their capacity to sustain their receptor potential during a continuous deformation: (1) In the Pacinian corpuscle and the receptors allied to hair displacement, a rapid adaptation or reduction in the electrical response takes place. There are some data which suggest that the adaptation, rather than being a property of the nerve itself, is due to changes in the tissue surrounding the nerve ending. (2) The second class, the slowly adapting receptors, occur frequently in the kinesthetic system, where they are able to signal the steady position of a joint.

The receptors for touch are unevenly spread over the skin. A high concentration is found on the tips of the fingers. It has been estimated that on the thumb the minimum amount of energy necessary to produce a sensation of pressure is of the order of .03 erg. While this amount of energy is exceedingly small, it is from 100 million to 10 billion times higher than thresholds in hearing and vision. This relatively low sensitivity of the skin is, perhaps, of some benefit to us. Geldard (1962) used very sensitive instruments that can detect and record microwaves on the surface of the skin. He found that the beating of the heart, breathing, and other internal events generate small waves along the skin with an amplitude of .001 to .05 mm. Fortunately, these stimuli are too slight to be perceived.

Our skin, however, is sensitive enough to hold some possibility as an alternative "hearing" mechanism for the deaf. Geldard (1957) has conducted research on the possibility of exploiting touch as a communications link. He placed five vibrators in contact with the fingers of a subject's hand and presented a code composed of three intensity levels and three durations of vibration. At the time of the report, one subject, at least, had reached a "reading" level of 38 words a minute.

Perhaps the reading rate could be increased if temperature changes were used as an added variable. Our skin is extremely sensitive to a change in temperature. We are capable of perceiving a change of less than one hundredth of a degree per second.

There is still some doubt concerning the identification of the particular receptors in the skin which respond so sensitively to temperature changes. The particular sensation produced by temperature change is generally dependent upon the direction of the change rather than the actual temperature itself. An increase in temperature leads to a sensation of warmth, a decrease, to cold. Perhaps you have tried the classic experiment of starting with one hand immersed in a bucket of cold water, the other hand in hot water. If both hands are then shifted into a bucket of lukewarm water, it will feel warm to the hand previously in the cold water and cold to the hand from the hot water.

The sensory nerves coming from the skin include fibers that change their firing rate only with changes in temperature. Some increase and some decrease their rate of firing when the temperature of the skin is raised within normal limits. This dual system of neural coding may explain some of the peculiar sensations that result from unusual stimulus presentations. If alternating thin strips of slightly warm and slightly cool temperature stimulate the forearm, one will experience a sensation of intense heat. In this situation, both types of temperature fibers will increase their firing rate—one type in the warm strips, one type in the cool strips. The type of fiber which normally increases its firing rate with a decreasing temperature, however, also shows a rapid increase in firing at very high temperatures. Thus, with either a very high temperature or with alternate cool and warm strips, both types of fibers will fire at an increased rate. Since most people have never before been subjected to an alternating temperature stimulus, the feeling of intense heat is an understandable outcome.

There is also a dual coding system in the kinesthetic system, one simple and one complex. The simple part of the system is in the joints, and the complex part is in the muscles.

The data presented in Figure 4 show the method by which a single

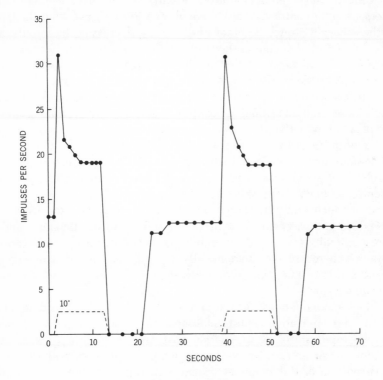

Figure 4

A graph of the changes in the neural impulse frequency from receptors sensitive to movements of the joints. The rise and fall of the dotted lines indicates when 10° changes were made in the angle of the joints. (Boyd and Roberts, 1953.)

neuron signals both the movements and steady positions of a joint. This impulse pattern comes from what are called spray-type endings in the capsules of the joints. Each receptor covers about a 15°–30° range of movement, with some overlap of ranges. These joint receptors provide a beautifully simple coding of our body posture. (Although the available data are all recorded from a cat's knee joint, most investigators assume this system is used in other joints and in higher vertebrates.) It was previously believed that the muscle-stretch receptors, within the muscle tissue and its tendons, were the primary information source for kinesthesis.

However, the impulse rate from these receptors is a complex function of (1) the length of the muscle, (2) the force exerted by the muscle, and (3) the changing level of modulation from an efferent pathway that originates in the spinal cord and goes out to very small muscle fibers adjacent to the stretch receptors. Stimulation of these efferent neural fibers causes a contraction of the small muscle fibers reducing the stretch of the adjacent stretch receptor and thereby decreasing its impulse rate, independent of a change in the angle of the joint. It seems fortunate that we also possess receptors that "hang out" in the joints, away from the hustle and bustle of the muscles.

It also seems fortunate that the input to the central nervous system from touch and kinesthetic receptors, although involved in a host of complex reflex activities within the spinal cord, arrives at the cerebral cortex with its virtue (simplicity) intact. Mountcastle (1961) describes single-neuron response patterns in the somatic sensory areas of the cortex which are quite similar to those recorded from neurons with specialized receptor endings in the skin and muscles.

For touch and kinesthesis (as well as the other cutaneous senses), ascending pathways—in the spinal cord and up to the thalamus and the upper lateral areas of the cerebral cortex—operate in an interesting manner. There are two anatomically separate systems which serve different sensory functions: the *medial-lemniscal* system and the *spino-thalamic* system.

The medial-lemniscal system provides an excellent coding of the spatial and intensitive aspects of touch stimuli as well as the temporal aspects—rapid shifts in stimulation that are so important for a useful position sense and an active touch sense. A primary property of the touch portion of the lemniscal system is its representation of body form: Each first-order neuron innervates a small region of the body surface, called its receptive field; the regional specificity of its information is preserved at thalamic and cortical levels. The ability to discriminate between two points 0.1 inch apart lightly touched to the skin in sensitive regions of the body (such as the fingertips) is explained by the large degree of overlap existing in these receptive fields.

There also seem to be inhibitory interactions betwen adjacent areas on the skin. Mountcastle (1961) reports recording single units in the lemniscal portion of the thalamus which increase their firing rate when one spot on a monkey's forearm is touched but show a great reduction in this rate when surrounding spots are touched. The properties of small, overlapping receptive fields—surrounded by areas of inhibition—probably underlie the fantastic discrimination required for a task such as reading Braille. The blind reader of Braille printing runs his fingertip along the line of raised letters rather than taking each one separately—touch discrimination seems to improve when it becomes an active process in time. Gibson (1962) has studied this active touch process as it is used in discriminating minor differences in the shape of small, solid, hand-sized objects. The subject, in "looking" at the shape tactually, keeps fingering it for a minute or so. The process whereby serial impressions from five different fingers eventually lead to an accurate concept of the shape of a complex object with blob-like protrusions probably takes place in integrative circuits of the cerebral cortex. This process would seem impossible without the accurate coding of complex temporal patterns of stimulation—coding that Mountcastle has found in the responses of single cells at the thalamic level.

The second ascending system, this one for tactual more than kinesthetic stimuli, presents an entirely different picture. It is called the *spinothalamic* system and responds to thermal and painful stimulation as well as tactual. The receptive fields of single neurons within this pathway in the spinal cord are generally much larger than in the lemniscal system. At the thalamic level, single cells from this system often respond to stimulation anywhere on the surface of the body. They also lack specificity as to the type of stimulus: the same cell will respond to painful, mechanical, and even auditory stimulation.

The role of the spinothalamic system is more a matter of responding to the general qualitative nature of cutaneous stimulation than responding to fine spatial and temporal patterning as the lemniscal system does. The spinothalamic system also serves an arousal function and influences the circulatory, digestive, and hormonal systems. When we walk into a cold room, we not only become aroused but our circulatory system makes certain compensatory adjustments. For this we don't need a fine discrimination of the locus of the cold or its exact temporal characteristics.

There are many interconnections between the spinothalamic and lemniscal systems and the vestibular pathways. When it's all put together we find ourselves with an admirable system capable of unbelievable feats—juggling objects with a stick in the mouth, with both hands and one foot, while balancing on some precarious perch with the other foot. More typically though, what the vestibular, kinesthetic, and tactual systems are doing is relating our bodily posture and movements to the relevant aspects of the environment as perceived with the visual, auditory, olfactory, and gustatory systems. Eating food is one process in which all of these things come together. Maybe that's why most of us enjoy eating so much.

VISCERAL SENSATION

The last part of the internal environment left for study is, perhaps, the most difficult. The subject matter of internal sensation impresses one with the unity of mind and body and the fantastic interplay between them. In 1859, Claude Bernard introduced the concept of the *milieu intérieur* to physiology and then spent the rest of his life trying to understand the "how" of the concept. His general approach is stated in the following passage in a translation by H. C. Green (Bernard, 1957). "... The external phenomena which we perceive in the living being are fundamentally very complex; they are the resultant of a host of intimate properties of organic units whose manifestations are linked together with the physicochemical conditions of the internal environment in which they are immersed. In our explanations we suppress this inner environment and see only the outer environment before our eyes."

A significant role in the regulation of the physicochemical conditions of the internal environment is played by receptors in key parts of the environment. While stimulation of many of these leads to conscious sensations, there are a large group which form reflex connections in the spinal cord and brain stem and have no direct conscious referent. Figure 5 represents the wide variety of sensory and motor functions related to these receptors. Although most of them are part of the sympathetic and parasympathetic divisions of the autonomic nervous system, some of the pathways subserving pain are somatic. (See C. M. Butter, *Neuropsychology,* in this series).

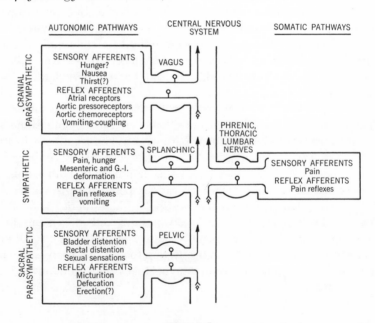

Figure 5

A diagram of the origin and function of the autonomic and somatic neural paths from the internal organs and skin respectively.

Most of the visceral receptors are either mechanoreceptors or chemo-receptors. There are dual afferent pathways from these receptors to the spinal cord: Typically, one pathway enters the spinal cord at a level related to the position of the viscera it innervates, while the second path may have a widespread entry. These pathways run beside the paths for cutaneous sensation to the cerebral cortex. There are separate cortical areas for the vagus, splanchnic, and pelvic nerves (Fig. 5), and these areas are quite small in relation to the auditory and visual portions of the cerebral cortex. Seemingly this is in keeping with their lesser impor-tance in consciousness.

So far, things appear quite simple and straightforward. This happy state of affairs can persist only as long as we stick to anatomy. The physiological processes which keep our internal environment within its necessary bounds have a degree of complexity which requires investi-gators to apply systems analysis, an approach used in engineering. This involves, among other things, the writing of simultaneous equations for the events at the multitude of control points within a complex system. The complexity of the physiological control processes is a result of the large number of separate, but interrelated, types of regulatory pathways. Aside from the receptors in the viscera, there is an increasing body of data related to receptor-like cells within the central nervous system, especially in the hypothalamus. Another type of control is the endocrine system. Several hormones seem to directly stimulate neurons in the brain; conversely, some brain cells seem to secrete their own hormones into the blood stream. These neuro-secretions influence such things as the repro-ductive cycle, water balance, and the heart rate.

As an illustration of the complexity of dealing with just one physio-logical variable, let us consider some work on temperature regulation. Nakayama, Eisenmann, and Hardy (1961) recorded impulses from single cells in the hypothalamus while inducing very small temperature changes just in the region of the recording electrode. They found cells whose firing rate would increase three times with only a 1-degree temperature increase. The local heating also resulted in changes in the respiration rate: a 2-degree increase raised the rate from 48 to 120 per minute.

With facts like these added to an already large store of quantitative information on temperature regulation, the experimenters derived a model of the total system using a systems-analysis approach. From a series of simultaneous equations they also developed an electronic analog whose circuitry is depicted in Figure 6. The point of including this rather frightening diagram is to illustrate the complexity and tremendous num-ber of interconnections between the various control points (represented by boxes and triangles). It is also included to show that complexity should not be thought of as raising impossible barriers to understanding.

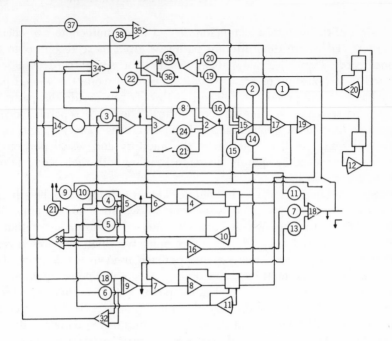

Figure 6

An electronic analog of the mechanisms for physiological temperature regulation. Each triangle and square represents a separate control function which can be duplicated with an electrical circuit. The lines between them represent their interconnections. (From Nakayama, Eisenmann, and Hardy, 1961.)

The simultaneous equations on which it is based were solved, with the aid of a computer, to predict the changes in various temperature-regulation variables when a human was subjected to a rising temperature. The predictions were all extremely accurate.

In the light of the complexity of analyzing the regulatory processes of just one physiological variable, can you imagine what the total system must look like? It seems legitimate to ask: Why all this complexity?

For many years, the emphasis in the study of *homeostatic* mechanisms (physiological regulatory processes), has been on the organism's need for maintaining constancy. The term itself implies this. If constancy were all that were necessary, it would be difficult to justify the complexity of the regulatory processes. There is an increasing appreciation of the fact that when the internal environment is constant the organism is dead (Brobeck, 1963).

Our body temperature goes through a daily rhythm, and, for women, a monthly rhythm; we eat and drink periodically; our blood sugar level is always changing; we are active or passive. This dynamic view shifts the whole role of the regulatory processes from a simple one of maintaining constant levels to a much more complex one of both governing and adapting to the durations and amounts of changes that take place.

One of the primary elements in this kind of system is an extensive set of receptors sensitive to changes in physiological variables. Although some of the control mechanisms take place without the direct participation of specific receptors and the central nervous system, the latter play a central role for the majority of controls. The more information supplied to the central nervous system from all its peripheral and internal receptors including those within the brain, the more sensitive will be the regulatory processes. Brobeck (1963) has pointed out the advantages, for accurate temperature regulation, of knowing both the rate at which heat is being gained and the rate of its loss, rather than just knowing the temperature.

The role of coordinating the multitude of regulatory processes within the brain seems to fall primarily on the hypothalamus and the limbic system. Since an animal can keep alive and maintain proper eating patterns after removal of its cerebral cortex, much less emphasis has been placed on the role of the cortex in regulatory mechanisms. However, even though the regulatory system is already quite complex, it would seem to need this additional complexity as well.

Pavlov's conditioned-reflex methods have been applied to this question by Russian physiologists (Bykov, 1957). They have demonstrated the formation of connections between unconditioned reactions of the bladder, kidney, liver, heart, etc., and various conditioning stimuli. In a typical experiment, a dog is surgically prepared with a tube inserted into the duct coming from its gall bladder so that its secretion of bile can be measured. Once a day the dog is brought into the experimental room, placed on a table and given an intravenous injection of a substance that produces an increased outflow of bile. This is the unconditioned response being made to the unconditioned stimulus, the injected substance. After six days of this procedure, the dog increases his biliary secretion upon just being brought into the experimental room and placed on the table. This is the conditioned reflex; it has become conditioned to the stimuli of the experimental room. On some days the conditioned reflex is larger than the original unconditioned reflex. The Russian physiologists have always maintained that the new connections between neural elements that form the conditioned reflex are located in the cerebral cortex. Although it has been possible to produce motor-conditioned reflexes of the leg flexion variety in a dog without its cerebral cortex, there is no evidence that the conditioned reactions of the internal organs are not cortically mediated. Thus, this seems to be a legitimate demonstration of the direct influence that can be exerted on visceral functioning through circuits in the cerebral cortex.

CONCLUSION

In returning to the cortex, we have returned, in a way, to the notions presented at the beginning of this chapter concerning the relation between the processing of information from the external world and the processing of that from our internal world.

I have tried to clarify as much as possible the differences and similarities between (1) neural input concerned with our own bodily condition and activity and (2) neural input concerned with conditions and events in the environment.

The perception of external events is distinguished by a definite state of awareness and a greater rate of information flow than that accompanying the perception of internal events. However, the similarities between internal and external input seem more important than the differences. The major similarity is a functional one: Both sets of inputs contain the determinants of ongoing behavior. The constantly changing conditions of the *milieu intérieur* serve to modify drive states and levels of motivation, which, in turn, serve to initiate and guide ongoing behavior; the resultant motor activity is heavily dependent upon further input from the touch, kinesthetic, and vestibular modalities. The perception of external events both governs the particular choice of action sequences and has its own motivating properties as reflected in behavior influenced by such things as art, music, good food, or a beautiful day.

Deeply ingrained in both types of input is an affective component, a set of feelings which also serve as their own determinants of behavior. The limbic system, with its input from virtually every sensory system, both external and internal, and its discharge pathways to the hypothalamus, is of prime importance for the feeling or emotional connotation in all experience.

Lastly, the functional similarity is also reflected in the brain-stem reticular system, which serves to modify the level of arousal. The reticular system receives inputs from all of the sensory systems, internal and external, any one of which may change the arousal level.

While it is a relatively simple matter to sit down and construct rather sweeping statements like the above, and just as easy to pooh-pooh such generalities and ask for the facts, I hope the reader realizes the necessity for both approaches. It is painstaking experimental work—under conditions controlling or eliminating all but the desired stimulus and response variable—which builds up, piece by piece, the anatomical and functional properties of a part of the over-all system. Such data must form the bedrock of sensory psychology. There is also a necessity for taking a serious look at the impossible complexities of ongoing behavior—at the bee returning to the hive from its food-finding flight and communicating the location of the food through an elaborate dance; at the salmon returning from the sea to the lake where it was hatched; but, most importantly, at the activities of people. We need to make some kind of guess about sensory processes in terms of the gamut of human behavioral processes. I hope the reader understands the facts well enough to feel free to tackle the big issues in his own terms and to keep searching for more facts.

REFERENCES

Bernard, C. *An Introduction to the study of experimental medicine.* (Trans. H. C. Green.) New York: Dover, 1957.

Boyd, I. A., and Roberts, T. D. M. Proprioceptive discharges from the stretch receptors in the knee joint of the cat. *J. Physiol.,* 1953, *122,* 38–58.

Brobeck, J. R. Review and synthesis. In Brazier, M. A. B. (Ed.), *Brain and behavior, Vol. II. The internal environment and alimentary behavior.* Washington, D. C.; Am. Inst. of Biol Sci., 1963.

Bykov, K. M. *The cerebral cortex and the internal organs.* (Trans. and Ed. W. H. Gantt.) New York: Chemical Publishing Co., 1957.

Gernandt, B. E. Response of mammalian vestibular neurons to horizontal rotation and caloric stimulation; *J. Neurophysiol.,* 1949, *12,* 173–184.

Gibson, J. J. Observations on active touch. *Psychol. Rev.,* 1962, *69,* 477–491.

——————. The useful dimensions of sensitivity. *Amer. Psychol.,* 1963.

Loewenstein, W. Biological transducers. *Sci. Amer.,* Aug. 1960.

Mountcastle, V. B. Some functional properties of the somatic afferent system. In Rosenblith, W. A. (Ed.), *Sensory communication.* New York: John Wiley, 1961.

Nakayama, J.,Eisenmann, J. S., and Hardy, J. D. Single unit activity of anterior hypothalamus during local heating. *Science,* 1961, *134,* 560–561.

ADDITIONAL REFERENCES

Dill, D. B. (Ed.). Adaptation to the Environment. *Handbook of Physiology,* Section 4. Washington, D. C.: Amer. Physiol. Soc., 1964.

Fraenkel, S., and Gunn, D. L. *The Orientation of animals.* New York: Dover, 1961.

Geldard, F. A. Adventures in tactile literacy. *Amer. Physiol.,* 1957, *12,* 115–124.

——————. *Fundamentals of psychology.* New York: Wiley & Sons, Inc. 1962.

Gellhorn, E., and Loofbourrow, G. N. *Emotions and emotional disorders: A neurophysiological study.* New York: Harper & Row, 1963.

Hess, W. R. *The functional organization of the diencephalon.* New York: Grune & Stratton, 1957.

Mason, E. *Internal perception and bodily functioning.* New York: International Universities Press, 1961.

Nafe, J. P., and Kenshalo, D. R. Somesthetic senses. *Ann. Rev. Psychol.*, 1962, *13*, 201–224.

Rose, J. E., and Mountcastle, V. B. Touch and kinesthesis. In Field, J. (Ed.), *Handbook of Physiology*, Vol. I. 387–430. Washington, D. C.: Amer. Physiol. Soc., 1959.